INDIANS

OSCEOLA, *Clark*
POCAHONTAS, *Seymour*
PONTIAC, *Peckham*
SACAGAWEA, *Seymour*
SEQUOYAH, *Snow*
SITTING BULL, *Stevenson*
SQUANTO, *Stevenson*
TECUMSEH, *Stevenson*

NAVAL HEROES

DAVID FARRAGUT, *Long*
GEORGE DEWEY, *Long*
JOHN PAUL JONES, *Snow*
MATTHEW CALBRAITH PERRY, *Scharbach*
OLIVER HAZARD PERRY, *Long*
RAPHAEL SEMMES, *Snow*
STEPHEN DECATUR, *Smith*

NOTED WIVES and MOTHERS

ABIGAIL ADAMS, *Wagoner*
DOLLY MADISON, *Monsell*
ELEANOR ROOSEVELT, *Weil*
JESSIE FREMONT, *Wagoner*
MARTHA WASHINGTON, *Wagoner*
MARY TODD LINCOLN, *Wilkie*
NANCY HANKS, *Stevenson*
RACHEL JACKSON, *Govan*

SCIENTISTS and INVENTORS

ABNER DOUBLEDAY, *Dunham*
ALBERT EINSTEIN, *Hammontree*
ALECK BELL, *Widdemer*
CYRUS McCORMICK, *Dobler*
ELI WHITNEY, *Snow*
ELIAS HOWE, *Corcoran*
ELIZABETH BLACKWELL, *Henry*
GAIL BORDEN, *Paradis*
GEORGE CARVER, *Stevenson*
GEORGE EASTMAN, *Henry*
GEORGE PULLMAN, *Myers*
GEORGE WESTINGHOUSE, *Dunham*
HENRY FORD, *Aird and Ruddiman*
JOHN AUDUBON, *Mason*
JOHN BURROUGHS, *Frisbee*
JOHN DEERE, *Bare*
LEE DeFOREST, *Dobler*
LUTHER BURBANK, *Burt*
MARIA MITCHELL, *Melin*
ROBERT FULTON, *Henry*
SAMUEL MORSE, *Snow*
TOM EDISON, *Guthridge*
WALTER REED, *Higgins*

SOCIAL and CIVIC LEADERS

BETSY ROSS, *Weil*
BOOKER T. WASHINGTON, *Stevenson*
CLARA BARTON, *Stevenson*
DAN BEARD, *Mason*
DOROTHEA DIX, *Melin*
FRANCES WILLARD, *Mason*
J. STERLING MORTON, *Moore*
JANE ADDAMS, *Wagoner*
JULIA WARD HOWE, *Wagoner*
JULIETTE LOW, *Higgins*
LILIUOKALANI, *Newman*
LUCRETIA MOTT, *Burnett*
MOLLY PITCHER, *Stevenson*
OLIVER WENDELL HOLMES, JR., *Dunham*
SUSAN ANTHONY, *Monsell*

SOLDIERS

ANTHONY WAYNE, *Stevenson*
BEDFORD FORREST, *Parks*
DAN MORGAN, *Bryant*
DOUGLAS MacARTHUR, *Long*
ETHAN ALLEN, *Winders*
FRANCIS MARION, *Steele*
GEORGE CUSTER, *Stevenson*
ISRAEL PUTNAM, *Stevenson*
JEB STUART, *Winders*
NATHANAEL GREENE, *Peckham*
ROBERT E. LEE, *Monsell*
SAM HOUSTON, *Stevenson*
TOM JACKSON, *Monsell*
U. S. GRANT, *Stevenson*
WILLIAM HENRY HARRISON, *Peckham*
ZACK TAYLOR, *Wilkie*

STATESMEN

ABE LINCOLN, *Stevenson*
ANDY JACKSON, *Stevenson*
DAN WEBSTER, *Smith*
FRANKLIN ROOSEVELT, *Weil*
HENRY CLAY, *Monsell*
HERBERT HOOVER, *Comfort*
JAMES MONROE, *Widdemer*
JEFF DAVIS, *de Grummond and Delaune*
JOHN F. KENNEDY, *Frisbee*
JOHN MARSHALL, *Monsell*
TEDDY ROOSEVELT, *Parks*
WOODROW WILSON, *Monsell*

Woodrow Wilson

Boy President

Illustrated by Mel Bolden

Woodrow Wilson

Boy President

By Helen Albee Monsell

the NEW *Bobbs-Merrill* COMPANY, INC.
® AN ASSOCIATE OF HOWARD W. SAMS & CO., INC.
Publishers • INDIANAPOLIS • NEW YORK

LIBRARY OF CONGRESS CATALOG CARD NUMBER: 59-14004

PRINTED IN THE UNITED STATES OF AMERICA

To Eudora Elizabeth Thomas,
my favorite librarian

Illustrations

Full pages

                                                        PAGE

Hawkeye Tommy knelt behind the trunk.   26

"She caught hold of a piece of rope."   35

On the gray mare's back sat Tommy.   66

Tommy marched down the aisle.   91

Their arrows flew through the air.   105

It was a wild battle.   137

He was standing by General Lee.   165

Tommy jumped as he reached for it.   172

"I'll make a trip across the country."   191

Numerous smaller illustrations

Contents

PAGE

That Means War! 11

Company's Coming! 22

When Mother Was Little 29

Mr. Moderator! 37

Blackberries Are Ripe 47

"I Wish I Had a Horse" 57

Anxious Days 71

Why Read? 82

On Sunday Afternoon 94

Wild Indians 101

Streetcars 111

PAGE

The Lightfoot Club 118

President Tommy 130

Three Cheers for the Circus! 140

A Subject for a Debate 150

General Lee Comes to Town 159

Good-by to the Lightfoot Club 168

Moving to Columbia 175

Princeton Days 180

Woodrow, the Man 186

Books by Helen Albee Monsell

DOLLY MADISON: QUAKER GIRL

HENRY CLAY: YOUNG KENTUCKY ORATOR

JOHN MARSHALL: BOY OF YOUNG AMERICA

ROBERT E. LEE: BOY OF OLD VIRGINIA

SUSAN ANTHONY: GIRL WHO DARED

TOM JACKSON: YOUNG STONEWALL

TOM JEFFERSON: BOY OF COLONIAL DAYS

★ # Woodrow
Wilson

Boy President

That Means War!

It was a crisp cool morning in the fall of 1860. The sun was shining down on the little city of Augusta, Georgia. A stiff breeze was blowing. It caught the leaves from the big tree by the gate and tossed them around the yard. Tommy Wilson's puppy was chasing them. When Tommy looked down from the upstairs window, he could hardly wait to get outdoors himself.

He ran to the head of the steps, slid down the banister and raced through the hall. Then he stopped. There was a smell of hot molasses cookies in the air. Maybe he'd better go by the kitchen on his way out.

11

Mother was rolling out the cooky dough on the table by the window. Old Mitty, the cook, was putting a fresh batch in the oven. The pan she had just taken out was on the back of the stove.

Tommy didn't even have to ask. Mother smiled at him and nodded her head. "They're hot," she said. "Don't burn your fingers."

Mitty ran a knife under three of the biggest cookies and lifted them from the pan. "Here."

They were so hot that he had to keep tossing them from one hand to the other.

"Don't play too hard," said Mother as he started toward the door. "You mustn't wear yourself out."

The puppy came racing to meet him. "Yap!" she said in a tone which plainly meant, "Cooky, please!"

"Wait a minute," said Tommy. "Let's see if they are cool enough to eat."

He bit into one of the cookies. It was only
pleasantly warm now.

"Here! Ask for it."

The puppy sat up on her hind legs. "Yap!"
she said again.

Tommy tossed her a big piece of cooky. Then they raced together down the walk. Father and a friend were just coming in the gate. Tommy nearly bumped into them.

"Hold on there," said Father. "Look where you're going." But he wasn't cross. He was only laughing. Father was never cross with Tommy. Now he spoke to his friend as if Tommy were a man instead of a four-year-old boy.

"This is my son, Thomas Woodrow Wilson."

The man looked at Tommy. "That is a right big name for such a scrap of a boy."

"It is indeed," said Father. "So we call him Tommy."

DOES THERE HAVE TO BE WAR?

Tommy didn't like to have anyone think he was "a scrap of a boy." He didn't like to have Mother tell him, "Don't play too hard." He

14

wanted to show everyone that he was really big and strong. He looked up at the gate. It was very tall.

"I am going to climb it," he decided. "That ought to show them."

But Father and his friend had gone on into the house. There was only the puppy to watch him. Maybe that was just as well. He had to try quite a few times before he reached the top of the gate. He didn't have much breath left. "I reckon I'll sit on one of the gateposts and rest for a while," he told himself.

More people than usual were going by. They looked worried and excited. Tommy wondered if there could be a fire uptown. He started to climb down from his post so that he could run and see.

Just then two men passed close by.

"Lincoln has been elected," one was saying. He sounded angry.

"Yes," said the other. "Lincoln has been elected. That means war."

They both looked so worried that Tommy felt worried, too. What did it all mean?

When Tommy was bothered about anything, he always went straight to Father. Father would

16

stop to explain things, no matter how busy he was. Tommy hurried up the walk now. He ran up the steps, across the porch and into the big hall. The door to Father's study was open. He and his friend were sitting in front of the fireplace. They were busy talking. They sounded worried, too.

"Father," Tommy began, even before he reached the door, "who is Lincoln? Why is there going to be a war?"

He hoped Father would laugh his big, jolly laugh and say, "Stuff and nonsense. Who has been filling your head with such foolishness?" Then everything would be all right again.

But Father didn't laugh. He looked as worried and upset as the two men had been.

"Mr. Lincoln," he said, "is going to be the next President of the United States. He has been elected by men who want to make the Southern states give up their slaves. A good many men in the South think slavery is wrong, too. But they want to take care of the question in their own way. They aren't going to let anybody *make* them do anything."

Tommy nodded. He knew that feeling very well, himself.

"The Southern states have said they would withdraw from the United States if Mr. Lincoln was elected. They believe they have a perfect right to do so. The Northern states say they haven't. They will fight to keep them in."

"Look here," said Father's friend. "What is the use of trying to explain things to the boy? He's too young to understand."

"Maybe so," said Father. "But then again, maybe he'll remember it later, even if he doesn't understand now."

Tommy bit into his last cooky. "Does there *have* to be a war?" he asked.

"I am afraid so," the friend answered before

Father could speak, "although it does seem as if there ought to be some other way out."

"There is," said Father. "Men who aren't selfish and who try to understand one another don't fight. But the world has never been willing to try that way."

"No," the other man said sadly, "and it never will."

"I am not so sure. Someday a leader may arise——"

"What is a leader?" asked Tommy.

"A man who can show the people what to do and make them want to do it."

"Just like the game the big boys play—Follow the Leader?"

"Exactly, Tommy. Now run outdoors and play. We will be busy for a while."

Tommy turned away thoughtfully. He was still thinking about what his father had said about war. As he opened the door he saw Joe

Lamar from next door coming up the walk. Tommy forgot all the questions that had been tumbling about in his mind.

"Can you come out, Tommy?" asked Joe. "Phil has to stay in the house. He went out of the yard when he wasn't supposed to. Now I don't have anyone to play with."

The two boys ran to the back yard and began to roll and tumble in some leaves that had been raked into a pile. The puppy wanted to join in the fun. She ran from one boy to the other, yapping excitedly.

After a while Tommy's sister Annie, who was two years older, came to find him.

"Oh, there you are, Tommy!" she said. "Goodness, you're dirty. It's time to come in and get ready for dinner."

Tommy ran ahead of Annie into the house. As he looked into the study, he saw Father and his friend still talking seriously.

Tommy started upstairs. Father's friend had been right. He didn't understand everything Father had tried to explain. But Father had been right, too. Even if he didn't understand entirely, some of the things Father had said stayed tucked away in his mind. "Someday a leader may arise——"

Company's Coming!

THE MEN in the street had been right. War was declared between the North and the South. At first it didn't seem to be the terrible thing Tommy had been afraid of. Sometimes he forgot about it. So many other interesting things were happening!

Almost a year had gone by when he came downstairs one summer morning to find the kitchen full of odors. He could smell chicken frying, pies bubbling, cakes baking.

"We're going to have company," his sister Annie told him.

"As if I couldn't guess it!" said Tommy.

Father was a minister. He was always having company. Usually Tommy was glad to see people come. Today, though, he wasn't the least bit glad.

"We'll have extra good things for dinner," Annie reminded him. "Just smell."

"But not everything about having company is good. Will they stay all night?"

Annie nodded. "Just look at that long row of piecrusts. Ever so many people must be coming. Or else they are going to stay for a long time."

"But if they are here tonight, Father won't be able to read to us."

"I reckon not."

"And he left off last night at the most exciting place. The Indians have just captured Hawk-eye——"

"Tommy!" called Mother. "Will you run down to the garden and get me a few sprigs of mint?"

Tommy ran out to the kitchen garden behind

the brick wall. He was still thinking about the Indians and Hawkeye. "Maybe Marion will read to us," he told himself. Marion was his other sister. She was nearly twelve. "But she'll probably be busy helping Mother. There's always a lot to do when we have company."

Now he remembered another thing he didn't like about having company. Mother always wanted him to be dressed up. Sometimes she even made him put on his Sunday clothes!

HAWKEYE

As soon as he took Mother the mint, he slipped away next door.

"Let's play in your attic," he told the Lamar boys. "Maybe, if Mother doesn't see me, she'll forget about how I look."

The Lamar boys knew how he felt. Their father was a minister, too. "Even if it isn't Sun-

24

day, you can't play games very well if you have your Sunday clothes on," they agreed.

They went up to the attic to play. They watched through the window as the Wilsons' company began to arrive. One man came on horseback. Another came in a buggy. Two of them came from the steamcars. They all carried big carpetbags.

"That means they are going to stay all night." Tommy groaned. "I'll never find out how Hawkeye got away from those Indians!"

"Let's play Indians," Joe suggested. "You be a white man. Phil and I will be Indians. We'll hide behind Grandfather's trunk. Then we'll jump out and scalp you."

"No, you won't. Because I am Hawkeye. I've got my rifle——"

"We'll have war clubs——"

"Come on. Let's start."

"Ye-ow!" shouted Big Chief Joe. He grabbed

up a feather duster and began to dance a war dance around the attic.

Hawkeye Tommy knelt behind the trunk. He used an old broom for his rifle.

Bang!

Phil had been creeping up behind him. Now he jumped on Tommy with a yell that sounded like an Indian war whoop.

"Boys! Boys!" called Mrs. Lamar from the foot of the attic steps. "Won't you please play something quieter?"

That ended the big fight. The boys sat down on the old trunk.

"What *can* we play?" they grumbled. "There isn't anything that's fun that doesn't make a noise."

Tommy had an idea. "Let's play church. I don't believe your mother will mind the noise if we are singing hymns. And we can take turns preaching."

They were just beginning to enjoy themselves again when Marion came to the foot of the steps.

"Tommy! Mother says it's time for you to come home."

Phil Lamar looked out the little window at the sun. "It isn't nearly dinnertime yet," he objected.

"We children will probably have dinner by ourselves, anyway," said Tommy. "What Marion means is that it's time to get me dressed up. I surely hope she isn't going to make me put on my new shoes!"

When Mother Was Little

It was a very neat and tidy Tommy who went into the parlor to meet Father's guests. Father put his arm around him. "This is my son," he told the men. "He was born on the twenty-eighth of December, 1856. We were living in Staunton, Virginia, then."

It was easy to see that Father was very proud of Tommy. Tommy was proud of Father, too. He was sure his father was the finest man there. He sat quietly for a while and listened, but sitting still was hard work. He wasn't sorry when dinnertime came.

The children had their dinner early. Then

they went outdoors to play. All afternoon they could see men coming and going at the Wilson house. Tommy was sure they had never had so much company in one day before.

Mother was still busy when suppertime came. She asked Marion to give the other children their bread and milk. "And then will you take them upstairs and keep an eye on them?"

Marion often kept an eye on the other children. She was Big Sister. Sometimes Tommy felt as if she were almost his second mother. She was almost as good as Mother, too, when it came to telling stories or answering his questions.

"Why are we having so much company at once?" he asked now.

"There's going to be a big meeting in Father's church. It begins tomorrow. Presbyterian ministers and elders are coming to it from all over the South."

"Will it last long?"

"Several days, I reckon."

"Through Sunday?" Tommy was worried. When a minister was a guest on Sunday, Father always asked him to preach the morning sermon. Suppose he asked all of the men here to preach!

"What is the meeting about, anyway?" he asked crossly.

"Well—we aren't in the United States any longer, you know," Marion told him. "Georgia is one of the Confederate States of America."

Tommy nodded. He was not quite five years old, but he knew that.

"And the Confederate States must have their own Presbyterian Church. Men have come from all the Southern states to get it started. They'll hold meetings in Father's church across the street."

"I wish they'd hold the meeting in some other church," Tommy said. "Then Father could go on reading to us about Hawkeye."

"No, he couldn't. He'd have to be at that other church, wherever it was."

Tommy knew she was right. He didn't even try to argue. Instead he started off on a new idea. "You go get the book and read it to us."

"I can't. It's in Father's study and some of the men are talking there."

"Then tell us a story. Tell about the time Mother was nearly drowned."

"Wait a minute," Annie said. "I want to hear it, too, but I want to get my doll first."

Marion sat down in a comfortable low chair. When Annie came back she sat on the rug, close by. Tommy lay down on the floor between them.

"Now we're ready."

A STORMY VOYAGE

"When Mother was a little girl," Marion began, "she lived over in England. Grandfather was a minister, just like Father. He had a big family. There were four brothers and sisters older than Mother. There were three younger than she was."

Four older brothers and sisters to take care of you and make you mind! Tommy was very fond of his older sisters, but he sympathized with little-girl Mother.

Marion sympathized with the big brothers and sisters. "It does seem as if the four of them could have kept an eye on little Jessie," she said, "but of course there were little James and Gene and Marion to look after, too. When I think how much time it takes to help Mother look after just you, I can understand how they felt with four youngsters on their hands.

"When Mother first remembers, they lived in a little house with a garden which went right back to a castle wall. She and Uncle James used to throw their ball against the wall. But when

Mother was eight years old, Grandfather decided to come to America. They sailed in a little packet ship, and they were on the ocean for over two months!"

"I'd like that," Tommy said.

"No, you wouldn't. Not when a storm was tossing the boat around as if it were a cat playing with a ball. And the winds were roaring and the waves were dashing——"

Tommy wriggled excitedly. This was the best part of the story. It always gave him shivers.

"Little-girl Mother didn't like it. The passengers were told to stay down in the cabin. She didn't like that, either. It was too hot and close and sticky. At last she managed to slip away.

"She climbed up to the deck. She wanted some fresh air, but the wind was so strong it almost took her breath away. It nearly blew her across the deck. She caught hold of a piece of rope.

"Just then a big wave came. She could see it,

like a big, green moving wall. She screamed, but the wind was too loud to let anyone hear her little voice. Then the wave struck.

"It buried the bow of the boat in the water. It swept Mother off her feet and washed her overboard. Her mouth was too full of water now to scream, but she held tight to the rope. It pulled her arms almost out of their sockets. It burned her hands, but she held on. She swung out far over the water. She could see it boiling and green below her. Then she swung back. She managed to catch at the railing. Then she crept back down to the cabin."

Tommy had been holding his breath. It was as good a story as an Indian story would be.

"So now Mother is afraid of the ocean," Marion finished. "And I don't blame her."

"I don't, either," Tommy agreed. "But I'd like to go on the water myself."

Mr. Moderator!

THE NEXT morning the Wilsons were up early. With four guests in the house there was work for everyone—Mother, Mitty, Annie, Marion, Tommy. Even the dog dashed around as if she were going on important errands.

Things grew quieter after the meeting started in the church. In fact, they grew too quiet. Tommy sat down on the porch steps, with the dog at his feet. The Lamar boys had gone somewhere to play. Everything was very still. He wondered what was happening in the church. Maybe Father was making a speech. Suddenly he made up his mind he would go see.

The meeting of course was for men, not boys. There was a big gallery, though, where the servants sat on Sunday mornings. Tommy knew where the stairs were. He could slip up to the gallery and sit on the floor behind the railing. The men downstairs couldn't see him, but he could see and hear everything.

He jumped up. He ran across the street and into the big church. Nobody was in the vestibule. He slipped up the dark stairs and into the gallery. He looked down.

One of Father's guests was standing by the pulpit. He wasn't preaching a sermon. He wasn't even talking. It was very plain, though, that he was in charge of everything.

Anyone in the church who wanted to speak would stand. "Mr. Moderator!" he would call.

"Dr. Palmer."

Then Dr. Palmer would speak.

Sometimes three or four men would jump to their feet at once. "Mr. Moderator!" they would all call.

Then "Mr. Moderator" would have to decide which one was first. "Dr. Hoge has the floor," he would say.

"I make a motion——"

It was very plain that Mr. Moderator kept things in order. Without him, everyone would be talking at once. Nobody would know what was happening. He had charge of the whole meeting.

"I'd like to be Mr. Moderator," Tommy decided.

Tomorrow he and the Lamar boys would play having a meeting instead of church. Only how did Mr. Moderator know what to do next? He would have to ask Father.

40

He was so interested watching that he didn't know how long he had been there. At last someone said, "Mr. Moderator, I move the morning meeting be adjourned."

Tommy wasn't sure what that meant. While he was trying to decide, everybody stood up. The meeting was over! It was dinnertime.

A GOOD ROMP

The meetings lasted nearly two weeks. Tommy slipped up the gallery steps nearly every day to watch and listen. But he was glad when they were over. There were ever so many questions he wanted to ask Father. Besides, he wanted his family to himself again.

Father took his last guest down to the steam-cars. As they were getting into the buggy, he looked at Tommy. "Do you want to come along?" he asked.

Of course Tommy wanted to go along. He climbed into the buggy. He sat quietly all the way to the station. It was very hard for him to sit quietly. He was rather proud of himself.

He liked the noise and bustle at the station. He wished he were going on the train. But maybe, after all, it was just as well he couldn't go. When the train had left they drove back home. Now Tommy had Father all to himself. He could ask all the questions he wanted to ask.

"Why did they call the man in front 'Mr. Moderator?' "

"He was the man in charge of the meeting. Sometimes he is called 'President' or 'Chairman.' We Presbyterians call him a moderator."

"How does he know what to do?"

"There are certain rules for him to go by. They are the same all over the country. They have a long name—parliamentary law."

Tommy liked long words. "Parliamentary

law." He said it over and over under his breath. He liked the way it rolled over his tongue. "Par-lia-men-tary law."

The mare knew she was headed home. There were oats waiting for her there. Tommy had so many questions to ask he wanted to go slowly, but the horse had other ideas. In almost no time she had them home again.

"Come into the study," Father said. "I'll show you the rules a moderator must follow."

In the study Father showed him a small black book. "These are our *Rules of Order*. When you can read, I'll give you a copy." He put the book back in his bookcase. "Now run along and get ready for supper."

Tommy felt cramped and stiff after his ride in the buggy. Besides, Father hadn't played with him for days. And there was plenty of time before supper.

"It's early yet," Tommy said.

"You need plenty of time. You're such a little slowpoke."

"Slowpoke, yourself!" teased Tommy. "You can't catch me!"

Father was tired of sitting still, too. He was ready for a romp. He made a dive for Tommy.

They ran through the big hall, across the porch, down the steps, and into the yard. Now they raced around the big snowball bush. Tommy tried dodging. Father could dodge, too.

Mother and the girls came to the window and stood there laughing. Finally Father chased Tommy into a corner of the yard. Tommy had one last idea. He began to climb the fence. Father caught him by the leg.

"I've got you now!" he crowed.

Both of them were breathless with running and laughing as they started back across the yard. *Rules of Order* were fun, Tommy decided, but this was more fun still.

The most fun of all, though, came that night. Supper was over. Mother sat in her low chair, knitting. The two girls sat on the sofa near by. Tommy turned a chair upside down near the candle table. Then he lay down on the floor.

He started to ask Mother to tell a story. But she would probably just get to the exciting point when Father would come in.

He jumped up and ran into the next room. When he came back he brought Mother's guitar. "Let's sing," he said.

Mother played the guitar softly. The children sang "The Minstrel Boy to the War Is Gone." With the second verse another voice joined in. Father had come from his study. He had a book in his hands. The song broke off in the middle of the verse.

"Now," cried Tommy, "we'll learn how Hawkeye got away from the Indians!"

45

Father liked to sit on the floor almost as well as Tommy did. He sat down by the candle table. He leaned back against the upturned chair.

"'When the Indians recognized their prisoner——'" he began.

Tommy wriggled happily. Mr. Cooper had certainly written a good book when he wrote *The Last of the Mohicans.*

Blackberries
Are Ripe

"Hey, Tommy!" called Joe Lamar. Tommy was up in the big oak tree. He hooked his arm over a limb and leaned down to call, "Come on up!"

"You come on down instead. Let's go blackberrying."

It was such a good idea Tommy wished he had thought of it himself. He climbed down to the lowest branch, swung by his arms and jumped.

"Wait until I get a pail," he said.

"Get a big one. Will Fleming says the berries are thick out his way."

Will was one of Tommy's friends who lived

out in the country. "I went out there last year," Tommy remembered, "when the berries were ripe."

He hurried to the kitchen. "I want a pail," he told Mitty.

Mother was busy by the kitchen table. "Don't make it too big a pail," she said. "You aren't strong enough to carry a heavy one, dear."

"But I am, Mother! I'm not a puny baby any more. I'm almost eight years old!"

"You're still thin and scrawny," said Mitty.

Tommy knew she was right, but he hated to be reminded that he wasn't strong. "I'm never exactly sick," he insisted. He wouldn't admit even to himself how tired he got doing the things the other boys did.

"Here is a pail that is middling big," said Mitty. "I hope you fill it. If this war doesn't hurry up and quit, there won't be anything for anybody to eat anywhere."

"GO GET YOUR MULE!"

The war had been going on for three years now. Tommy could hardly remember when it had started. At first it had only been something which was happening far away. Now, every day, it was coming closer and closer. There were almost no young men left in town. They were all in the army. Father wasn't home very much. He was off preaching to the soldiers and helping take care of them.

"There's one good thing about the war," Tommy told Joe as they started for the gate. "All the schoolteachers are in the army. We'd be shut up in some schoolroom this very minute if they weren't."

"You're right," Joe agreed. "But the army needs more men still. Hey, wait a minute. There come some now."

Down the road came a small troop of men. "They're off to join the army," said Joe.

The boys climbed up on the gateposts to watch them pass.

"They surely don't look like soldiers now."

Some were riding old horses. Some were on mules. Some were trudging through the dust on their own feet. Some of them were in their best clothes. Others were almost in rags. But they

were all in a good humor. They joked with the boys as they passed by.

"Hey, bub," called one, "aren't you afraid you'll fall off that post?"

Tommy grinned. "Oh, go get your mule!" he called back. That was a new bit of slang he had just learned. He was rather proud of it.

The soldiers-to-be laughed. They trooped on down the road. Tommy and Joe laughed, too, but somehow, after the men had gone by, it didn't seem so funny.

"That man probably has a boy of his own back home," Tommy told Joe.

"I reckon nearly all of them do. If they didn't have families, they would have been in the army long ago."

"Their wives are going to have a hard time taking care of the children by themselves."

"And the boys are going to miss their fathers."

"I wish this war would end," said Tommy.

"So do I," Joe agreed.

"I wish we didn't have to have wars."

It was nearly four years since the day when Father had explained to Tommy about war. He couldn't remember it well enough to tell Joe. But he still felt as he did then, and, dimly, he remembered what Father had said. "Someday a leader may arise——"

Both boys sat still for two or three minutes. Then Tommy climbed down. "Well," he said, "we'd better be getting along if our folks are going to have blackberries for dinner."

IT IS NO FUN TO GO BLACKBERRYING

"You always *think* blackberrying is going to be fun," Tommy fussed some two or three hours later. "You take the biggest pail your mother will let you have. And then you find out all over again that it isn't fun at all.

"The sun gets too hot. The briers scratch you. Mosquitoes, gnats, and other kinds of bugs bite you. Besides, it takes just about sixteen million berries to fill a pail. And the more you pick, the heavier the pail is going to be when you carry it home."

Joe stood up and stretched. "And the best berries are so low you have to break your back picking them," he added. "Or else they are so high you almost stretch your arms out of their sockets reaching for them. And then the brier slaps you in the face when you let it go."

"And I'm thirsty, tired, hungry, and hot. And I have a stone bruise on my foot."

"Well, our pails are full, anyway. Let's go home."

They crossed the stubble field, back to the road. There the dust was soft to their bare feet. But the pails seemed to grow heavier and heavier as they trudged along.

"It's funny," said Tommy. "Right now, both of us feel as if we never want to go berrying again as long as we live. But our mothers will put something on our bites and scratches, and we'll have a good dinner. Then we'll lie down on the grass under the apple tree and maybe Marion will read to us for a while. We'll forget how miserable we are right now. We'll be ready to do it all over again."

"I won't," said Joe.

"By tomorrow morning you'll be ready to go again," said Tommy. "Just wait and see."

"LET'S DO IT AGAIN"

Mitty was glad to get the berries. She looked at the clock. "There's just time to make a berry pie for dinner."

Mother looked at Tommy's legs. They were all scratched and bitten. "Come on upstairs and

54

wash them in cool water. Then I'll put some ointment on them."

When dinner was over, Tommy went out into the yard and lay down underneath the apple tree. A good breeze was blowing. He had never felt more comfortable. After a while Joe came over. He stretched out by Tommy. "We had blackberry pie for dinner," said Tommy.

"We had blackberry roll."

They lay sleepily quiet for a few minutes.

"My mother was mighty glad to get those berries," Tommy said.

"So was mine," said Joe.

"I'll bet you they are thicker behind the piney woods than in the bushes where we were."

"Um-hum. And remember that snake that crawled out from the bushes? Maybe we could catch him next time."

"If we went earlier in the day, we wouldn't get so hot," Tommy said.

"Shucks! I don't mind a little sun."

"I don't, either. It felt good on my back."

"Um-hum," Joe said. "You know, it's fun to go blackberrying."

Then both boys laughed. "What did I tell you?" crowed Tommy.

"Well, it is. You know it is, yourself."

"Of course I do. Let's go again tomorrow."

"I Wish I Had a Horse"

AFTER THE blackberry season was over, summer settled down to stay. In the fields outside the city, the cotton bolls grew fat. Then they burst into fluffy masses of white. Cotton pickers were busy from morning till night.

Tommy wasn't particularly interested in cotton. "I wish I had a horse." he told his sisters one warm Monday afternoon.

"I wish I had one, too," Annie said, "but there isn't a chance. Our soldiers need every horse that isn't being used on the farms."

"I know. But all the same it would be fun to go riding this afternoon."

"Would you rather do that than go walking with Father?" Marion asked.

" 'Deed I wouldn't. I'd just like to do both. Say—that gives me an idea!"

Both girls laughed. Tommy was always having ideas.

"It must be a mighty good one if it fixes things so that you can go riding and walking at the same time," Marion teased.

Tommy jumped up from the porch step where he had been sitting. He started down the path around the house toward the kitchen. "If Father comes out, tell him I'll be right back."

"I know where you're going," Annie called after him. " You want some of the cookies Mother made this morning from the molasses Aunt Marion sent her. Bring me some too."

Cookies were a rare treat these days. As the war kept on, even molasses was hard to get. Aunt Marion lived on a plantation just outside the city. Her daughter Jessie was just about Tommy's age. Tommy often went out there to spend the day with them. Aunt Marion knew how fond he was of cookies. She had managed to save a little molasses for Mother to use.

When Tommy came back from the kitchen, his hands were full. He divided the cookies with the girls. Then, instead of eating his own, he put them in his pocket.

"Why don't you eat them?" Annie asked.

"He's saving them for his walk," Marion said.

But Tommy only said, "Has Father come out from his study yet?"

Annie shook her head.

"I wish he'd hurry up. If he doesn't it will be time to come home before we start."

"Nonsense. You have the whole afternoon ahead of you."

"But Monday is always the shortest day of the week. It is three times as short as Sunday."

"You feel that way because on Sunday you can't run about or play games."

"Maybe," Tommy agreed, "but that isn't the only reason."

"No?" Marion was teasing again. "Could it possibly be because Father is too busy on Sunday to pay his son any special attention?"

Tommy grinned. "I reckon so. Anyway, we always have an extra good time on Mondays. You ought to see the places we go to—mills, railroad yards, factories. If Joe and I tried to get into places like that by ourselves, we'd be chased away in a hurry. But when Father tells a man, 'I'd like to take my son through your mill,' he is as pleased as a peacock. He shows us everything."

"That's because Father is a minister. Everybody likes him."

"I should say they do! Folks who say they wouldn't like to be a minister's son don't know what they are talking about. Really, it is a great deal of fun."

Just then Father came out. "Are you ready, Tommy? It is time we were off."

Tommy jumped up in a hurry.

"Where shall we go?" asked his father as they started down the steps.

Tommy decided he'd not say anything about his special idea yet. He'd just head their walk in the right direction. "You've never shown me how a cotton gin works," he suggested.

"So I haven't. And that is something every Southern boy should know. We'll go out to Mr. Fielding's plantation. It will be a warm walk, but I hear he started ginning yesterday."

THE IDEA WORKS

Augusta was a small city. Soon Tommy and his father had left its houses behind them. In

the fields on either side of the country road the cotton pickers were at work. They moved slowly down the rows, filling their big bags with the fluffy white cotton.

Tommy wasn't interested in the pickers. He wanted to get on to the cotton gin, but Father stopped to speak to everybody. It made Tommy as fidgety as a worm in hot ashes.

Finally they came to the gin shed at the far end of Mr. Fielding's plantation. There, on a shaft, was a great flat cogwheel. Two long poles, or sweeps, stretched out from the shaft. Horses were harnessed to these sweeps. They pulled them around and around. This turned the shaft. Other wheels fitted into the cogwheel. Belts connected them with the gin upstairs.

Now it was Father who pushed on ahead. He didn't notice that Tommy was pulling back. Father wanted to see the gin. Tommy wanted to see the horses. He climbed the narrow steps slowly. He looked back as long as he could see even the swish of the gray mare's tail.

"You must watch closely," said Father when they reached the gin room.

Tommy looked at the big box in front of him. Inside were two rollers. The first one was covered with saw teeth. When the gin man dumped a basket of cotton into the gin, it caught on those teeth and was carried through a grid. The grid was too narrow to let the seeds through. They were torn out and fell down a hole into the seed room below.

The second roller was covered with brushes. They brushed the seeded cotton from the saw teeth out into the lint room. Now the teeth were ready to bite into a new basketful of cotton.

"It's a wonderful machine," said the gin man. "When my father was a boy, cottonseed had to be picked out by hand. I've often heard him tell how he went over to the Widow Green's plantation just a short way from here, to watch the first cotton gin work.

"Mr. Eli Whitney was visiting her house and had invented it while he was there. It was a queer-looking contraption, Pa said. You had to turn it by hand. But even then it could do the

64

work of a half-dozen men. Why, before we had the gin, it took a good worker a whole day to pick a shoeful of cottonseed! This machine can clean as much in an hour as he could have done in a week!"

"Wonderful!" Father agreed. "And just think what it has meant to our whole country! More cotton, more trade, more factories——"

He and the gin man talked on and on. They quite forgot Tommy. At last it occurred to Father that his son was unusually quiet. He turned around. Tommy had disappeared.

"Now where has the young rascal gone?"

"Probably he's down in the shed, helping whip the dust from the cotton. Youngsters always like to use switches. Or else he's out watching the big screw press the cotton into bales."

But Tommy's idea had nothing to do with switches or screws. He had slipped away as soon as Father and the gin man started talking.

When Father came downstairs, he didn't see his son at first. Instead, he almost bumped into the man who drove the gin horses. Right now, the man seemed to be taking a rest. His hands and mouth were full of molasses cookies. He looked as happy as a cow in a cornfield.

The gin hadn't stopped working. The horses were still going around and around, pulling the sweeps. Father looked. There on the gray mare's back sat Tommy. He had traded his cookies for a ride on a gin horse.

"SAY JUST WHAT YOU MEAN"

The best part of Monday afternoon walks came on the way home. Then Tommy could ask all the questions he wanted to. That didn't mean just two or three. His questions lasted more than halfway home. After that it was Father's turn. He wasn't satisfied with just two or three questions, either. He wanted to make sure his son understood everything he had seen.

Tommy enjoyed that, too, especially when he knew the answers. Today it was hard at first to pull his mind away from the horses. Still, there were a good many things he wanted to know. Where did Eli Whitney come from? What became of him? Did he ever invent anything else?

Father had to wait quite a while for his turn. At last Tommy's father said, "Now tell me exactly how a cotton gin works."

When Tommy's father said "exactly," he meant "exactly." Tommy knew better than to use such words as "kind of" or "something or other" or "sort of like." His answers must be clear-cut and plain.

Today he had a fine new word he'd been saving for a week. Father would be impressed. "The wheel at the top of the shaft was absolutely stupendous."

Instead of being impressed, Father laughed. "What do you mean by that?"

"Why," said Tommy, "I meant 'very big.'"

"Then why didn't you say 'very big'? Remember this. Always use the word that means exactly what you want to say. If that word is a big one, use it. But you will find that nearly always small words say what you mean better than big ones do."

"Yes, sir," said Tommy. "All the same," he added to himself, "I think stupendous is a fine word."

"Now start again."

Tommy started again, but he still felt peevish. He didn't like to be laughed at.

"What becomes of the cottonseed?" Father asked.

"It falls into the seed room. Mr. Fielding saves enough to plant next year and throws the rest away. That looks like a big waste to me."

"It is. Men are trying now to make cottonseed cake which can be fed to cattle. Some folks even say that cottonseed oil can be made for human beings to use."

Tommy wasn't sure he would like that.

"How is the cotton weighed?" asked Father. "How is it cleaned?" Then finally came the last question: "What made the machinery run?"

At that, Tommy forgot to feel cross. "I did," he said proudly, "because I drove the horses."

Anxious Days

It wasn't only that the war was taking such a long, long time to end. It wasn't only that food was hard to get. Now people were looking at one another with anxious faces. How much longer could the South hold out? Suppose the South should lose?

Tommy couldn't suppose any such thing, but the war was making the whole world turn upside down, it seemed to him.

Sunday was, as Tommy very well knew, a day of rest. Nobody was supposed to work. The catechism said that it must be spent "in public and private worship, except for such parts as

71

were to be taken up in the works of necessity and mercy."

Father believed in the catechism. He saw to it that the Wilsons' Sundays were spent in just that way. He urged the people in his church to keep it that way, too.

But there came a Sunday morning that fall when Father prayed even longer than usual before he started across the street to the church. His face was set in strange new lines. The news all week had been bad, very bad.

Tommy crossed the street with Mother and the girls. The church seemed dark and dim after the glaring light outside. Everything was very still. It was hard to believe that a war was really going on.

There came the usual opening hymns and the long prayer. Then Father stepped forward to the pulpit. Tommy settled back for the sermon. It wasn't so hard to sit still as it used to be. He could understand nearly everything his father said now.

Suddenly he sat up straight in startled surprise. There was a quick rustle through the entire church. Everyone else seemed to be as surprised as Tommy was. Father was speaking, but he wasn't preaching a sermon.

His voice was clear and ringing. "There is a great battle raging today. Our men need ammunition. Immediately after this service you must go to the ammunition factory and help fill cartridges. You will now rise and receive the benediction."

Father was cutting the morning service short so that the people could go to work on Sunday! Tommy could hardly believe it. Then he remembered the catechism again. "Except for such parts as were to be taken up in the works of necessity." War was terrible. It could even upset Sunday!

Every day the news grew worse. Sherman's soldiers had reached Atlanta. They were starting their march to the sea. On that march they took everything their army would need. They set fire to everything they thought the Southern army could use.

Of course, other things caught on fire, too. When a blaze started, it spread over a whole farm. As the soldiers marched on, they left behind them home after home in burning ruins.

Augusta was only a small city, but there were big warehouses there. If the cotton in them could be sent to England, it could be sold for money to buy arms and supplies the Southern army needed. Would Sherman's army come to Augusta to burn the cotton warehouses? Nobody knew.

"But we'll find out mighty soon," Joe said to Tommy. "The Yankees are getting nearer."

The two boys had been on an errand for Mother. Now they were on their way home.

"Let's go down by the river," Tommy suggested. "It isn't much out of our way."

"Let's. I'll race you to the first warehouse."

Off they started, but when they reached the corner, Tommy stopped short.

"Look!" he cried. "What is happening?"

Men were dragging the heavy bales of cotton

from the warehouses. They were piling them in the street.

"It's the Yankees! They're here! They are going to burn the city!"

Joe shook his head. "They're not soldiers."

Tommy looked again. Joe was right. Most of them were too old for soldiers. And there was Dick Fulsom's brother, who had lost his arm at Manassas.

One of the old men had stopped to wipe his forehead with his sleeve. He gave the boys a tired grin. "Pushing cotton bales around is hard work," he said.

"Why are you doing it? We thought you were Yankees getting ready to burn the town."

"No, sirree, I'm not a Yankee. And nobody's getting ready to burn this town—yet. But there's no telling. Sherman's men may get here any time. We haven't much of anybody left to fight them. All our boys are in the army already."

76

He gave his shoulders a tired hitch and went back to his cotton bale. "So we thought we would get the cotton out in the road all ready for them. Maybe they would just put a match to it without burning the buildings.

"Then perhaps we could put out the blaze before the whole city caught fire. Maybe the idea will work. Maybe it won't. We don't know yet, but it's worth trying anyway."

A LONG NIGHT

That night as he lay in bed, Tommy could hear men marching past his home. They were going out of town, not into town. He jumped up and ran to the front of the house.

He peeped through the blinds into the moonlit night. "What is it?" he whispered anxiously to Mother.

"We've had word that Northern soldiers are

close by. The few men left in town have gone
out to meet them."

"Will there be a fight?"

"Let us pray not. But if there is, we must be
ready. The wounded will be brought back. We'll
use the church for a hospital. There will be hard

work then for the women and children to do. Right now, there is nothing to do but wait."

All that night they waited. Sometimes Tommy dozed. Then he would wake with a start. Had the Yankees come? There was no sound of fighting. The girls joined their mother and Tommy. They sat there, waiting, watching.

At last the gray light of dawn crept through the blinds. It was morning. Nothing had happened.

Soon after sunrise the men of the town came trooping back. They looked sleepy and rumpled after a night in the open fields. There had been no fight. The enemy soldiers had taken another road. They wouldn't come to Augusta, after all.

THE END

The long war dragged on. Slowly the end grew near. First came the terrible news that

General Lee had surrendered. Then General Johnston surrendered. Soon after that an excited man stopped at the gate.

"The Yankees have captured President Davis," he called to Father. "Some folks say he was dressed in his wife's clothes, trying to get away. But they nabbed him!"

After that, rumors came thick and fast. "They are going to bring President Davis through Augusta."—— "They are taking him up north to prison."—— "The carriage will come down this street!"

Tommy hung over the gate excitedly.

"Come into the house, Tommy," called Mother sternly. When he came up the porch steps she added, "It is hard enough on the poor man to be a prisoner. There's no need to make it worse by having the road lined with folks staring at him as if he were a wild beast in a cage."

Tommy went upstairs. The front blinds were

drawn to keep out the hot sun. He peeped through them. Down the street came a carriage. He could see Jefferson Davis, President of the Confederacy, sitting in it. There were soldiers on each side of the carriage.

The President, himself, was a prisoner. Now Tommy knew that the war was over.

Why Read?

SAD DAYS followed. Many of the men of Augusta who had gone to war never came back. They were dead on the battlefield. Those who did return were tired and discouraged. Some of them were crippled.

The slaves who had been freed were not ready for freedom. They were like children. Men were sent down from the North to help them, but some of these men only tried to make themselves rich.

It was a hard time for the people of the South, but the days were not all black. Now that they knew the worst, they could face it. The war was over. Their boys were no longer being killed in

82

battle. Life began to be filled once more with homey, everyday happenings.

The days were busy ones for Tommy. He was learning to read. "It is high time!" many of his mother's friends said. "The idea of a boy going on nine years old before he has even learned his letters! And a minister's son, too!"

They didn't understand. Tommy hadn't been able to learn to read as long as the war was going on. His eyesight was very poor. He needed glasses. To try to read without them would have strained his eyes still more. It might even have made him blind. But it was impossible to get glasses during the war.

"We'll just have to let his reading lessons go for a while," Father had decided. "There is plenty for him to learn without books. Besides, all of us can read to him."

Tommy liked to listen to other people read. He wasn't at all anxious to start reading for himself. But now the war was over. He had his glasses. They were a pesky nuisance! He couldn't play rough-and-tumble games for fear he would break them. The boys made fun of them. And worst of all, with glasses, he must learn to read.

Tommy liked to do things that none of the other boys could do. There was no fun in learning something they could already do better than he could.

"Will you hear Tommy's reading lesson for me this morning?" Mother asked Marion one warm summer day. "Your Grandfather Woodrow's train gets in at noon, and I shall be busy every minute getting ready for him."

The children knew how happy Mother would be to see Grandfather Woodrow again. He hadn't been able to come to Augusta during the war. Tommy could hardly remember him.

Marion was glad to help Mother, but it wasn't

easy to hear Tommy's lesson. He always wanted to argue about it.

"This primer is for babies," he told Marion. "What's the use of reading it? I know all the stories in it already."

Marion sighed. Tommy was *so* stubborn whenever he didn't want to do a thing. And he was right. The primer was babyish. Father had just finished reading one of Mr. Dickens' novels out loud to the family. Now he was reading Weems's *Life of Washington*. You couldn't expect a boy who enjoyed grown-up books like those to get any fun out of a primer.

"But you *have* to learn to read sometime," she told Tommy.

"I don't see why. I'd rather just listen to Father."

"He isn't always here."

"Then you or Mother or Annie can read to me."

"We won't be with you after you are grown."

"Then I'll learn to read after I'm grown. But right now I want to go play in the ditch by the church. The rain this morning filled it knee-deep."

"Mother wants you to read your lesson first."

"Oh, well, if I *have* to——"

With Marion's help he stumbled through the

lesson. Then he hurried to the ditch. The Lamar boys came over. Soon they were busy making boats out of leaves. They were sailing them when Grandfather Woodrow arrived. Tommy scampered up from the ditch in a hurry.

His grandfather was a small man, but he was almost as quick as Tommy himself. He had been born in Scotland and still spoke with a Scottish accent. It was hard at first to understand, but soon Tommy began to like it. Before Grandfather's visit was over he had begun to copy it, just a little.

"WILL YOU LEND ME YOUR GLASSES?"

Grandfather Woodrow came on Saturday. When Tommy awoke the next morning he had a feeling that it was going to be a good day. At first he couldn't think why. Then, all of a sudden, he remembered.

Grandfather was a minister. He would preach the morning sermon. Last night Tommy had watched him take his notes from his bag. The sermon wasn't going to be long.

After church they would all go to Aunt Marion Bone's plantation for dinner. Aunt Marion always had good dinners, but, with Grandfather visiting them, she would be sure to have something extra special. And, best of all, Sunday was a day of rest. There wouldn't be any reading lesson!

Tommy felt happy as he laced his shoes and slicked down his hair. This was going to be a good day!

There were a few bad minutes right at first. The minister's family sat only four pews from the front of the church. Everyone could see Tommy every minute of the service. They expected the minister's son to keep especially quiet. That wasn't what worried him. He had grown so used to that he didn't mind. But he did mind walking down the aisle with those glasses on.

Tommy knew he wasn't good-looking. He was too thin and wiry. His nose was long, his chin was sharp. "And when I put these glasses on," he groaned to Annie, "I must look like a big grasshopper."

But he wouldn't let the boys know he cared. He started down the aisle with his head held high. Will Fleming grinned at him as he passed. The boy in the pew ahead started to snicker. He managed to choke it back before his mother could notice, but Tommy heard him. His face grew red. He held his back straighter than ever.

"He'd be whispering names at me if he dared," Tommy thought to himself. "Huh! I can think of half a dozen good ones myself. 'Old Four-Eyes'—'Grandaddy Wilson'—'Tommy Frog-eye.'" He hoped he didn't look as miserable as he felt as he sat down by Mother.

After the first hymn he felt better. He liked to sing. The music made him forget about himself.

After the offering had been taken Grandfather Woodrow stepped forward. He put his notes on the reading desk. He felt in his pocket for his spectacles. A blank look came over his face. He felt in another pocket, then another. At last he turned to Father. They spoke for a moment in low tones. Then Father came forward.

"Dr. Woodrow has left his eyeglasses at home," he announced. "Will someone in the congregation lend him a pair?"

Every man in the church who was wearing glasses took them off. They brought them down the aisle. Tommy took off his glasses, too. He marched down the aisle with the men. None of the boys would snicker now. They would all envy him. He was sorry his pew was so far front. That made his march short.

Grandfather Woodrow tried on each pair of glasses without smiling. He chose the ones through which he could see best. With a polite "thank you" he motioned them all back to their pews. Then he began his sermon.

Tommy could hardly listen to a word he said. He was too interested in watching those glasses. They were too large. The day was warm. Grandfather's nose began to get moist with perspiration. The eyeglasses began to slide. Down they would come, all the way to the point of his nose.

Then, just when Tommy was sure they were going to fall off, up would go Grandfather's arm. He would push the glasses back in place without stopping a word in his sermon. For a moment they would stay still. Then they would start sliding again. Tommy grew so interested watching them, he was almost sorry when the sermon was over.

After church he stood by Grandfather. He heard him thank the owner of the spectacles when he gave them back. "I couldn't have read a word without them," he said. "And it is a very sad thing not to be able to read."

Marion looked at Tommy. Tommy grinned. "But Grandfather doesn't have to read just primer stuff," he whispered.

On Sunday Afternoon

Aunt Marion's dinner was just as good as Tommy had expected it to be. Fried chicken, rice and gravy, hot biscuits, baked tomatoes, with peach tarts to finish off—he ate and ate!

After dinner, though, came Sunday afternoon. None of the children ever enjoyed Sunday afternoons.

"We have to keep on our best clothes," Jessie fumed, "and sit around, with nothing to do."

"Even if we had on our everyday dresses," Annie reminded her, "we still couldn't *do* anything."

"That's right. I don't mind not climbing trees

or going into the woods, or wading in the creek on Sundays, but I do wish we could play games."

"We can play Bible games," said Tommy. "Let's try Guess Who."

The other children agreed. They sat down on the porch steps.

"I'm thinking of a boy in the Bible," Tommy began. "You can ask three questions. Then you must guess who it is."

"What did he do?" Annie asked.

"He tended his father's sheep."

"That's easy. We don't need three questions. It's David."

"That's right."

"Now it's my turn. I'm thinking of a man in the Bible. Ask your questions."

It was a good game, but after a while they couldn't think of any new names.

"Will it be a Sunday game if we use people in American history?" asked Jessie.

"I reckon that's all right," Tommy decided.

"Then I'm thinking of a boy in history. Ask your questions."

"Where did he live?"

"In Virginia."

"What did he do?"

"He cut down a tree."

"Oh! George Washington!"

"Father was reading to us last week in Dr. Weems's book about how Washington chopped down the cherry tree," said Tommy, "but some people say it is just a story and isn't really true. No one is sure that he really chopped it down."

"But Mother says," Annie told Jessie, "that it doesn't make any difference whether it is a true story or not. It *is* true that George Washington was the kind of boy who wouldn't let somebody else be blamed for what he did. He'd tell the truth and face whatever happened next."

"I don't see anything so extra special about

that," said Tommy. "Anybody can do that. Now the part of the book I liked best was when he was fighting with the Indians the time that General Braddock was killed. The bullets went whizzing through his coat——"

"Look," Jessie interrupted. "The next time

you come down on a weekday, let's play Wild Indians."

"Let's," agreed Tommy. "We'll make some bows and arrows——"

But just then Mother came out to the porch. "It's time to start home," she said.

"I'M READING"

Of course Monday couldn't be Tommy's day with Father while Grandfather was there. Neither could Tuesday or Wednesday. The *Life of Washington* lay unopened on the table. Tommy did wish they could go on with it.

"You read it to us," he begged Mother on Thursday.

Mother shook her head. "I want to be with your grandfather every minute I can."

"Then you go on with it, Marion."

"I'm busy." Marion laughed. "If you are so

tired of baby primers, why don't you read it to yourself?"

Tommy was startled. Reading was a lesson. It had never occurred to him that he could do it for fun.

He picked up the *Life of Washington*. Then he lay down on the floor near the table, where the lamplight would fall on the book. He opened it carefully. "When Washington saw that the Indians——" he read slowly.

He couldn't manage the big words, but there weren't very many of them. Why, he was really reading! At first he was as proud as a puppy with his first trick. Then he forgot all about himself. He was too interested in George Washington. Soon he was so deep in his book he didn't even hear the slow ticking of the big clock. He had no idea how time was passing.

At last Marion came back into the room. "Nine o'clock, Tommy," she said. "Mother says to tell you it's time to go to bed. You can read some more of that book tomorrow."

Tommy looked up in surprise. He shook his head. He might not always be stubborn about the same thing, but he could still be stubborn.

"I can't go to bed now," he said firmly. "I'm reading."

Wild Indians

NOT LONG after Grandfather's visit, Tommy's brother Joseph was born. Mother and the girls couldn't give all their attention to Tommy now. He wasn't sorry. It was good not to be the youngest child and the only boy in the family.

One morning his womenfolk were all busy with the new baby. Tommy decided he would go out to Aunt Marion's to spend the day. He and Jessie hadn't had that game of Wild Indians yet. He always liked to play with Jessie. She could run as fast as he could and climb just as high, even if she was a girl.

Now that the war was over, the Wilsons had

a horse again. Tommy had learned to drive. He would often take the reins when he and Mother started off together. He liked riding, though, even better than he did driving. The horse was big and black. She was so broad that when he sat on her back, his legs stuck out more than they did down. But he never fell off.

His puppy had grown to be a big dog now. She had puppies of her own. Tommy stopped to play with them a moment before he climbed up on the big horse. "It won't be long before you'll be running along with me when I ride off," he told them. "Then the rabbits along the way will have to watch out."

It wasn't a long ride to Jessie's home at Sand Hills. She saw him coming and ran to open the gate. She remembered their plan.

As soon as they put the horse in the stable, they hurried down to the thicket by the brook. They chose two long switches there for bows.

102

They found some reeds, too, to make into headless arrows. They sat on the back porch while they strung their bows with cord that Jessie had saved. This took quite a while, but at last it was finished. Tommy and Jessie stood up and tried out their bows and arrows.

Just beyond Sand Hills there was a strip of piney woods. Beyond the woods lived a large family of children.

"Sometimes they play Indian and chase me," said Jessie, "and sometimes I play Indian and chase them. It's a good game, no matter which side you play."

"Let's go down to the piney woods and hide," said Tommy. "Then if any of them come along, we'll give a war whoop and jump at them."

"We'll have to put on war paint first," said Jessie.

They ran down to the chicken yard. They got enough feathers to make their hair as wild as any

Indian's. Pokeberries were ripe. They stained their faces with rich purple pokeberry juice.

That meant hard scrubbing later. "It will be worth it, though," Tommy decided, "if I look as horrible as Jessie does. And I bet I do, only worse." He added another big dab of pokeberry juice.

Now the two Indians, in all their war paint, went down to the piney woods. They hardly had time to hide when through the woods came three children. Their mother had sent them to the store for some molasses.

"Sh," whispered Tommy. "Here come some unwary settlers. Is your bow ready? Now when I yell, shoot and then jump out at them."

The "settlers" came nearer. They were watching two squirrels chase each other. They didn't guess there were wild Indians close by.

"Ye-ow!" screamed Tommy. *Zing* went his arrow as it flew through the air.

Jessie screamed at almost the same moment. *Zing* went her arrow, too.

Of course, the arrows didn't hit anybody. The Indians hadn't meant for them to. If they did hit, they wouldn't do more than make a very little bruise. But the way they whizzed was as exciting as if they were really deadly weapons.

The settlers yelled. Then the Indians dashed on them. In another moment settlers and Indians were all screaming and chasing one another. It was hard to tell which were having the best time.

But the settlers' mother was waiting for her molasses. At last they had to go on.

TOO GOOD A SHOT

The Indians sat down on a log to catch their breath. "What shall we do next?" asked Tommy.

"Let's go to the house for some cookies."

That was a good idea. They went up to the house. A few minutes later they stood on the porch steps munching. Then Tommy had an idea.

"Let's play you are a squirrel and I am an Indian. I have a hungry squaw and three papooses back in my wigwam. I'll go behind the house and count to five hundred by fives while you hide. Then I'll come hunting for you."

Jessie darted to the front of the house while Tommy went back of the kitchen and started to count. She picked out a big maple with thick leaves that would hide her well. She climbed as easily as if she were a boy.

Soon Tommy came stalking through the woods. He looked up every tree. Finally he saw a flutter of blue. Jessie's dress was showing through the leaves. He drew his trusty bow and shot an arrow in the tree.

He didn't really aim at her. But just then Jessie

decided to climb to a higher branch. She was reaching up with one hand. The arrow hit her shoulder. It startled her. She lost her balance and tumbled down at Tommy's feet.

There she lay, white and still. Tommy was so frightened that for a second he couldn't move. He was sure she was dead.

"If I get my horse and dash home as fast as I can," he said to himself, "I'll be gone before anyone finds her. They will never know I did it."

But he couldn't just run away and leave her there. "I'll go call Aunt Marion," he decided. "Only I won't say I shot her. People will think one of the other children did it."

But while he raced toward the house he remembered the Sunday afternoon when they had talked about George Washington—how he wouldn't let someone else be blamed for what he did. "And I said," he remembered, "that I didn't see anything especially hard about telling the truth and facing what happened next. I know better now, but I'll have to do it."

"Aunt Marion," he called as he ran into the house. "Come quick! Jessie is dead! It wasn't an accident. I killed her!"

Aunt Marion and the servants came running. They picked up Jessie's limp little body. They carried her into the house and laid her on the sofa.

"Get some water," said Aunt Marion. "Go to my medicine chest. Bring me the tall bottle."

Just then Jessie's eyelids moved. She wasn't dead! Her eyes opened slowly. A minute later she was trying to sit up. "What happened?" she asked. Then she answered herself, slowly. "I— was falling—and I reckon—I bumped the breath out of me—when I hit the ground."

Sure enough, that was all that had happened. There were a few bruises, but not a bone was broken!

Tommy was so happy that he sang all the way home. Once or twice he gave a war whoop just to hear himself yell. But he didn't try to shoot a single arrow into the bushes along the roadside. No, sir! A boy who could hit a mark he wasn't even aiming at had to be careful!

Streetcars

THE CITY of Augusta was growing larger. Eleven-year-old Tommy could borrow Father's horse whenever he wanted to go farther than he could walk. But not everyone in town was so lucky. They needed streetcars.

All through the summer the boys had watched the workmen laying the tracks. The long metal rails glistened in the sun. Tommy could hardly wait to see the streetcars. At last, one evening, Father looked up from his paper.

"We'll have really up-to-date traveling in Augusta in a few days. I see that the streetcars have arrived. They are down at the carbarn now."

111

The next morning Tommy and Joe went down to see the streetcars. The carbarn was a huge building that looked like a shed.

"Look at that front wall," said Joe. "It is almost nothing but doors."

"It takes a big door," Tommy reminded him, "for a streetcar to go through."

"I know. Doesn't it look strange to see the tracks running right into a building like that?"

"I'm glad the mules are going to have such a fine stable," said Tommy. "They'll deserve it after they work hard all day. Just see those big cars they'll have to pull."

The streetcars were shining in their new paint. "They look like Noah's arks on wheels," said Joe. "Do you suppose just two mules can pull one of those big things—especially when it's full of people?"

"Sure! When they get on the tracks they run so easily I could almost pull one myself. And the driver puts on an extra mule at the foot of a steep hill."

The next day the streetcars were actually running. Tommy stood on the sidewalk and cheered when the first one went by. He wasn't satisfied, though, just to stand and watch. In less than a

week he and Joe had saved enough money to take a ride themselves.

They climbed up the steps at the back of the car. Inside were two long benches facing each other. Tommy sat on one side and Joe on the other. For the first few blocks they sat stiff and straight, staring at each other. They were as solemn and dignified as two wooden Indians. Then they began to grin. Then they got together on one side to look out the window.

They were still in their own neighborhood, but the houses and stores seemed different when they were looked at sidewise through a street-car window. Then the neighborhood itself changed. The car took them past great ware-houses filled with cotton. They went by the railroad shops. At last they came to the end of the line.

"How on earth are we going to turn around?" asked Joe.

114

"You wait and see," said Tommy. Father had explained it to him.

The car tracks ended on a low, round platform. The platform was sometimes called a turntable, because it could be turned around. The mules pulled the car onto the platform. Then they pulled the platform, with the car on it, around until the rails met again. Now the car was facing back toward town.

There were no other passengers as they started home. The boys stood in the front of the car and talked to the driver. He showed them how he worked the brakes when the car went downhill.

"Let us try it," begged Tommy.

"All right. Get ready. We're coming to a steep hill as soon as we turn this corner."

They turned the corner and started down the hill. The streetcar picked up speed on the smooth rails almost before the boys knew what was happening. Both of them grabbed at the brake. They got in each other's way. The car went faster and faster.

"Hey!" cried the driver. "Watch what you're doing!"

Tommy's hand closed on the handle. It wasn't a second too soon. Joe's hand was close by his. They pulled together. The brake squealed as the car slowed down.

"Whew!" said the driver. "In another minute we would have run into the mules and had them sitting in our laps. Now here is the end of the line, unless you boys want to take another round trip."

"Let's," said Tommy. "I'd like to try that hill again."

It was nearly dinnertime when they reached the home corner after the second trip. They put their fare in the little box in front and told the driver good-by as they climbed down the back steps.

116

That night the Wilson family sat out in their front yard under the trees. Far away they could see the lights of the streetcar bobbing slowly along. They looked like a string of colored lightning bugs.

"First of all, people walked," said Tommy. "Then they rode horseback. Then someone invented carriages for the horses to pull. Now there are tracks and streetcars. I wonder what someone will think up next?"

The Lightfoot Club

WILL FLEMING was coming to spend the day with Tommy. "I do hope he'll have a good time," said Mother. "You always have such fun at his house. It seems to me that there are many more things for boys to do out in the country, though, than there are here in town."

Tommy wasn't worried. "Will can always find plenty for us to do," he agreed. "But he can hardly ever get up a good ball game way out there. There aren't enough boys. Here we can start playing as soon as he comes."

"Maybe he won't be as anxious to play as you are," Marion suggested.

118

But he was. He was hardly in the yard before they were off again, with Tommy's bat and ball.

A short way down the street there was a vacant lot. Several boys were there already—Peter and Henry from down the street, the Lamar boys, Bob Smith, Dick Fulsom and others. They had already marked the bases.

"Hi, Tommy! Hello there, Will!" they called. "Hurry up. We're ready to choose sides."

Tommy and Will got on opposite sides. Tommy was first at bat. He missed the first ball. But he hit the next one. It rose high in the air. How Tommy ran! He touched first base and almost reached second. But Will was running, too. He made a beautiful catch. Tommy was out.

"Too bad," called Will.

It was Bob's turn next. He had hard luck, too. He struck out. Then Henry went to bat. He was tagged trying to reach second. Tommy's side had to go out into the field without having made a single run. The other side didn't do much better. One man reached first base, but he was left there. Soon it was Tommy's turn again. This time he made up his mind he would bat the ball clear into the next block.

The pitcher threw the ball. Then—*Crack!*

Even Tommy knew he couldn't have hit it that hard. Why, he hadn't hit it hard at all! The boys all looked up, startled. They had been too busy to notice the sky. Black thunderclouds were rolling up. A red flash of lightning zigzagged across the dark mass.

"We'd better run," said Bob.

"We can have one more inning," the others insisted.

The pitcher thought so, too. "Just time enough for me to put you out," he told Tommy.

He threw a hard, straight ball. Tommy struck. Then he ran—first base, second base, on to third. The ball went across the road and landed in the

120

bushes by the sidewalk. Peter was still hunting
for it when Tommy reached the home plate.

Then, just as Peter found the ball, the rain
came down.

"Run!" they all shouted. "We'll get soaked."

No one even asked, "Where shall we run?"
They all knew. They made a beeline for Tommy's barn and climbed the ladder to the loft.

A CLUB IS BORN

The barn loft was big and roomy, with great mounds of hay. Down below them the boys could hear the horse moving in her stall. A hen was nesting in the hay. She squawked angrily at the boys, then scurried away. The rain strummed on the roof over their heads. At first it almost drowned their shouts as they rolled and tumbled in the hay.

Finally, breathless, they lay down to cool off. The rain quieted to a gentle steady beat.

"No more baseball today," said Joe.

"You know what I wish?" asked Will. "I wish we could get up a regular team. I live a long way out, but I could get in to play with the rest of you. And we could play the boys from other parts of town."

Tommy had a sudden idea. "I tell you what! Let's start a club. We can have a name and a secret password and play baseball and make speeches and everything!"

"That's a good idea!"

"What will our name be?"

"The Rovers!"

"I don't like that!"

"The Wild Indians!"

"How about the Beavers?"

Everybody was talking at once. Nobody was listening to anyone else. One or two of the boys were ready to fight. They were making a great racket, but they were getting nowhere. Tommy remembered the meetings in Father's church. Those men had all been anxious to talk, but they managed better than this.

"Look here," he called to the boys. He jumped

up on a mound of hay. "Listen just a minute."
At last he got their attention. "If we're going to
have a club we must do it right. We'll have to
have parliamentary law."

Tommy wasn't the only boy who liked big
words. The others liked them, too. "What is
parliamentary law?"

The rain had slowed down now to a drizzle. "I'll run up to the house," said Tommy, "and borrow Father's *Rules of Order*. That will explain it."

He ran through the drizzle up to the house and knocked on Father's study door. When he explained what he wanted, Father got his *Rules of Order* from the bookcase. Tommy put it inside his shirt to keep it dry. Then he ran back to the barn.

The more he read to the boys, the more excited they became. This would be fun. It would be as good as play-acting. "Come on. Let's elect a president right now."

"Let's elect Tommy, because he already knows most of the rules."

They brought a barrel up from down below to use as a table.

"Now," said the new president, "the first thing we must do is make a constitution."

"Mr. President!" called Will.

"Mr. Fleming has the floor," said Tommy gravely.

"I move our president write the constitution and bring it to the next meeting."

Everybody yelled "Aye" before Tommy could put the motion. He didn't have time to object.

But he didn't want to. Writing a constitution would be work, but he would like to try it.

"Is there further business to come before the meeting?" he asked.

"Mr. President!"

"Mr. Fulsom."

"I smell ham frying. That means it is close to dinnertime. I move we adjourn until the constitution's ready."

That motion was never seconded, voted on, or passed. Instead the boys began to jump and climb down from the loft. They were hungry, and they didn't want to miss their dinners.

Tommy worked hard on the constitution. At last it was ready. He wasn't sure about all of the spelling, but he couldn't show it even to Father because this was a secret society. Even if the words did look queer, the boys wouldn't know any more about them than he did.

When it was finished he called another meeting in the barn. One of the boys brought a rolled-up poster with him. "This is a secret society," he said, "so we ought to have something to scare folks away if they try to peep in on us. I brought this to tack up opposite the ladder."

He unrolled the poster. "I made a picture of an Indian," he said. "I think that ought to scare folks away."

All the boys laughed. The poster was a picture of a fierce-looking Indian with a many-colored feather headdress. The Indian held an upraised tomahawk in one hand.

"Where's the hammer?"

The meeting had to wait until the poster was tacked in place. Then Tommy read the constitution. The boys voted on it, article by article.

"Now for a name."

"I move," said one of the boys, "that we be named the Lightfoot Club. It sounds like an Indian name, but baseball players need light feet, too."

"Is there a second to the motion?"

"I second it," said Peter.

"Is there any discussion?"

There was, indeed. The president had a hard time to keep only one boy talking at a time. Many other names were suggested. Finally a vote was taken. The Lightfoot Club won.

Tommy looked through one of the little openings in the gable of the barn. The sun was shining and the wind was blowing.

"Now," said President Tommy, "one of the main objects of the Lightfoot Club is to play baseball. It is good baseball weather. Do I hear a motion that we adjourn to the ball field?"

President
Tommy

IT WAS several weeks later. The Wilsons were at dinner. From his seat between Mother and Marion, Tommy could look through the window which opened on the side yard. He had seen more than one boy go by on his way to the barn. As soon as their president could join them, there would be a meeting of the Lightfoot Club.

It seemed to Tommy that dinner would never end. Father had a guest. They talked and talked. Tommy grew more and more impatient.

Mother had seen the boys going by the window, too. Finally she said in a low tone, "You may be excused, Tommy, if you want to go."

Almost before she had finished speaking, Tommy was at the door.

Up in the loft the boys were all talking at once. They seemed to be very angry at somebody about something. As Tommy climbed the ladder, he could hear Peter's voice above the others.

"And she said she'd sick her dog on us if she ever caught us in her yard again."

"She always was the meanest old woman in town."

"Her old apples weren't fit to eat anyway. They were green as grass."

"What's happened?" Tommy asked Joe.

"Peter and Henry were coming past Mrs. Jones's place just now, and they saw some apples lying on the grass under her big tree. There wasn't any sense in leaving them there for the chickens to peck, so they climbed over the fence after them. Mrs. Jones caught them and gave them a good dressing down."

"We'll get even with her," said Henry. "We have a plan, but you boys will have to help us."

"Of course we'll help."

"Tonight after she has gone to bed we'll get her cow out of the cowshed. We'll fix her up fine, with ribbons on her horns and an apron around her neck. Then—you know how high Mrs. Jones's porch is?"

The boys nodded. "There must be a dozen steps," Bob said.

"We'll coax and push the cow up the steps and tie her rope to the front doorknob. Then we'll ring the bell, bang on the door and run. When Mrs. Jones comes down and opens the door, she'll pull the cow right inside the hall."

"Say, it's too bad it will be too dark to see her face from where we'll be hiding. But I'll bet she'll screech so loudly that she can be heard across the river!" said Peter. "And she'll have a time getting the cow down those steps again!"

132

"It will serve her right, the stingy old thing!" Henry said. "Making such a fuss over half a dozen wormy apples!"

"But they were her apples, after all," Tommy remarked.

"Yes—and it's going to be her cow, too!" said Peter.

The boys laughed. Tommy grinned. "I can't help feeling, though, that it is rather hard on poor old Bossy," he said.

That hadn't occurred to the boys before. "We wouldn't really hurt her," said Peter. But he didn't sound positive.

"My father says a man's house is his castle," Tommy went on. "And I reckon a woman's yard is, too."

"I never thought about it that way," Henry said, "but maybe you're right."

"Besides, if we're going to play tricks on any-one, we ought to choose somebody our own size.

A dozen boys against one little old lady—it really doesn't seem quite fair."

By this time most of the boys were beginning to feel that perhaps their trick wasn't such a good idea after all. Peter, however, was not yet quite ready to admit it.

"I'm not going to let Tommy Wilson tell me what to do and what not to do."

Henry laughed. "Tommy never does that. Somehow, though, he always manages to make us see things his way. Well, let's forget the cow and get along with the meeting."

"I'm ready," said Tommy. He banged on the barrel. "The meeting will please come to order."

A PINE CONE BATTLE

It was a short meeting. The weather was too fine for the boys to want to stay inside. Besides, President Tommy had a new game to suggest.

134

"After the rain this morning the field is too wet for baseball. Let's go down to the strip of piney woods back of Henry's house and have a pine cone battle. Half of us will be on one side of the path through the woods and half on the other."

The boys hurried down the street to the strip of piney woods. There Bob and Tommy were made the captains. Then they began to choose their sides. Tommy picked both Peter and Henry for his side.

"Now," said Joe, "we must decide on the rules of battle."

"If a man is hit by a cone, he's killed and has to drop out," Tommy suggested. "If he slips and falls he is a prisoner. The pine tags are so slippery we'll have plenty of prisoners. You keep yours back of those bushes, Bob, and we'll keep ours on the other side of the ditch.

"A prisoner can't fight until he escapes and

gets back on his own side of the path. If he's hit by a cone while he's escaping he's killed, but if he gets back safe he can fight again. The last man left alive wins the battle for his side."

"Come on, let's get ammunition," cried Bob.

The boys chased through the woods, gathering pine cones. Then Bob called, "Ready?"

"Wait a minute," said Tommy. "I'll have to take off my glasses."

"Now—one, two, three, *fire!*" cried Joe.

It was a wild battle. With whoops and yells they drove each other back and forth across the path. They ducked as the pine cones whizzed over their heads.

Without his glasses Tommy couldn't aim any too well. He was a good dodger and ducker, though. Nobody could hit him. One by one, as the boys were "killed," they dropped out. Then they stood back behind the bushes or the ditch and cheered their side on.

"There he goes, Bob!"

"Watch out, Tommy!"

At last only Tommy and Bob were left. Bob was hiding behind a tree. Tommy was crouched down behind a blackberry bush. Neither would show enough of himself for the other to aim at.

"They can stay like that all night," the other boys groaned. "We'll just have to call it a drawn battle."

But Tommy had another idea. He hung his cap on a stick. Then he stuck the stick in the ground so that the cap showed just a little above the bushes. He crept a few feet away.

Bob saw the cap. He thought it was on Tommy's head. He aimed and fired. His cone hit the cap and knocked it to the ground. "I've got him," he cried, jumping from behind the tree.

Then he saw the stick and knew he had been tricked. He jumped back, but it was too late. He had given Tommy a chance to aim and fire, too. Even without his glasses Tommy couldn't miss at such close range. His cone struck Bob squarely on the shoulder. The game was over.

"We've won!" cried Peter. "We've won!"

He had forgotten all about being angry with Tommy. As they trooped back up the street, they passed Mrs. Jones's yard. It was late afternoon. She was just driving her cow into the shed.

"There goes Mrs. Jones," said one of the boys. "And there goes her cow."

"Let her go," said Peter. "When Henry and I play tricks we'll pick someone our own size, not just a little old lady." He honestly believed it was his own idea!

Three Cheers
for the Circus!

THE LIGHTFOOT CLUB had a good summer. The boys played teams from other parts of town. They held secret meetings, with the Indian poster on guard. But when the days grew shorter the boys began to grow gloomy. It was almost schooltime.

"If the war hadn't ended," Peter grumbled, "the teachers would still be in the army."

"They were in there too long," said Henry. "That's the trouble. They brought home all sorts of army ideas about discipline. Take Professor Derry, for instance. Look at the way he makes us toe the mark!"

140

Tommy felt anxious. His eyes were stronger now and his health was better. Now that he was nearly thirteen, it was time for him to begin Latin and Greek. He was to start in Professor Derry's school the next week.

"Don't worry," Joe told him. "You'll get along all right. Why, a bookworm like you will probably enjoy it!"

But he didn't. It was true that Tommy was a bookworm. When he became interested in a book, he wanted to keep on reading. Mother would only smile when she saw his lamp burning long after he was supposed to be asleep. "We mustn't be too hard on him," she would say. Mother was a bookworm herself, so she knew how Tommy felt about reading.

Professor Derry had very different ideas. He expected Tommy to keep on reading, too, but it mustn't be only in the books he liked. It must be in Latin and mathematics and Greek as well.

He never said, "We mustn't be too hard on the boy." He said, "We mustn't be too easy if we expect Tommy to learn his lessons."

"Oh, I know it is good for me," Tommy grumbled. "I have common sense. And Professor Derry is fair. To tell the truth, I believe I like him. But that doesn't mean I like the ruler he uses when I can't recite. And it doesn't mean that I like his cane, either."

"Things could be worse," Joe admitted. "We're lucky to be so near the cotton warehouses that we can play there during noon hour. And it's good so many of the Lightfoot boys are in the same school. That means we can keep up our baseball games."

THE CIRCUS PARADE

The winter wasn't bad, but when springtime came the boys grew restless. "Why can't you

142

think up something new to do?" the Lightfoot Club asked its president.

One day a man came through town in a buggy. He had a big roll of posters at his feet and a bucket of paste. Before he drove on, he had posted notices all over the city. The circus was coming to town!

Not many circuses had been able to come south during the war. Few of the boys had ever seen one. They hadn't been so excited since the day the streetcars started running.

The day of the circus four of the boys were talking about it on their way to school.

"My cousin saw it in Macon. He says there's an elephant."

"Father says they have big torches so that they can have a show at night as well as in the day-time."

"I wish I could be a clown."

"I'd rather be a lion tamer."

"There's going to be a grand parade at ten o'clock."

"It won't do us any good. We'll be in school."

"Aw, I want to see the lions!"

"And the elephant!"

"And the ladies in spangled dresses!"

"And the clowns!"

Tommy knew perfectly well that he could go to the circus. If he hadn't saved up enough money for a ticket, his father would give him the rest. But right then the parade seemed more important than the circus itself. It came first. If he wasn't there, other people would see some of its wonders before he did. Besides, the boys had been wanting something new to do.

"Let's not go to school this morning," he said suddenly. "Let's go to the parade instead."

The boys were startled. Then some of them grinned. "Say—that's not a bad idea. But we'll catch it when we get back."

"What if we do? It will be worth it."

They hid their books behind some bushes. Then they started uptown. They couldn't go through the business section. Their fathers might see them. They couldn't go past the homes of any of the club members. Their mothers might be looking out the windows. It was a roundabout trip, but at last they reached the street down which the parade would come.

Quite a crowd was there already. The boys climbed onto a fence and perched there, like so many roosting chickens. Now that they had time to think they began to feel a bit worried. But it was too late to back out. The school bell had rung long ago.

At last they heard music. It was faint and far away. Then it grew nearer. They could see the band wagon. Men in bright uniforms were tooting and blowing and beating a big drum.

"Look! Yonder's the elephant!"

"Just look at those horses!" cried Tommy.

The parade passed slowly by—wild animal cages, trained dogs, clowns, everything. It was a good parade. There were ladies in fine sparkling dresses. The clowns turned handsprings. The wild animals roared. The boys enjoyed every minute of it.

146

Finally the last cage rumbled by. The women who had brought their little children to watch the parade turned away. "It's all over," they said.

It wasn't over for the boys. They jumped down from the fence. They rushed ahead until they caught up with the band. Then they marched along with it all the way to the circus grounds. There the parade broke up. Now it was really over. The boys looked at one another.

"Well," said Tommy at last, "I reckon it's time to go back and face the music."

The way back seemed very, very short. They didn't talk much. They were thinking about Professor Derry's cane.

Tommy put his hand in his pocket. "Hey!" he said. "I have a good-luck horse chestnut in my pocket. I traded my old knife to Peter for it the other day. Maybe if we rub it, it will give us luck." He took out the horse chestnut and passed it around. Each boy gave it a hard rub.

Just then they were going by the cotton warehouse. Tommy had another idea. He ran inside and came back with some big wads of waste cotton. "Here! We'll stick this cotton in our clothes where it will do the most good," he said. "It will soften the blows that we are sure to get from Professor Derry's cane."

The boys padded one another until they were so plump their seams were almost bursting. Then they went up the steps to Professor Derry's classroom.

Professor Derry looked at them. He looked at his big watch. "Take your seats," he said.

Tommy was tired. The day was warm. The cotton padding was warmer still. But he wasn't anxious to have school close. It seemed as if the time had never gone so quickly before.

At last Professor Derry closed his book. "The boys who played truant will remain. The rest of the class are dismissed." He reached for his cane.

148

It was some time later when the boys came down the school steps.

"Your lucky horse chestnut didn't do us a bit of good," they told Tommy.

"No," Tommy agreed. "The cotton didn't help much either." Then he grinned. "But it surely was a good parade."

A Subject for
a Debate

AFTER the circus, life grew rather dull again.
One fall day the boys had a club meeting. "Let's
do something new," the boys insisted.

Tommy thought it over. "We might have a
debate," he suggested. "All colleges have debate
teams. If we practice now we'll have a better
chance to get on one of the big teams when we
go to college."

The Lightfoot boys liked the idea. "Maybe
we can get up debates with some of the boys
from other parts of town, the way we do baseball games," Phil suggested.

"We'll have to practice first," Peter said. "Let's

choose a subject and each of us get ready to debate it. Then we'll have a debate of our own and ask Dick Fulsom's brother to be the judge. He's been to college. He can choose the two best men, and we'll send them out against the other clubs."

Everyone liked that idea. There was a chorus of approval. Tommy rapped on the table sharply. "I think that's a good idea, too," he said. "But if we ask Dick's brother, we'll really have to work. We don't want him to think he's wasting his time."

After more discussion the boys agreed that Tommy was right. They really had to dig in. They set the time for the debate. It was to be next Friday in the Wilson barn.

Choosing a subject wasn't easy. Each boy had his own ideas. Suggestions came thick and fast. Tommy had to rap for order again and again during the discussion.

Peter wrote down all the subjects as they were suggested. Bob insisted that "Honesty is the best policy" would be good. Joe was equally sure that "Robert E. Lee is the greatest living American" was the best subject.

At first everyone agreed with Joe. Tommy smiled with relief when all the boys seemed satis-

fied. "Now who wants to be on the side to prove that General Lee is *not* the greatest American?" Tommy asked.

There was dead silence for a moment. Then murmurs of "Not I" and "I don't want to" came from all the boys.

Tommy took off his glasses. He polished them on the front of his shirt. Then he put them back on. He knew that General Lee was the hero of every boy in that room. Tommy couldn't imagine himself trying to prove that Robert E. Lee was *not* great. He rapped for order.

"We can't have a debate without two sides to a question," he said slowly. "I guess we all feel the same way about General Lee. Maybe we should choose another subject."

"Yes! Yes!" all the boys said.

Tommy said, "Let's choose a subject that really has two sides this time." Then the boys settled back to think. At last they agreed on an idea. The subject would be, "Resolved: That the pen is mightier than the sword."

The meeting broke up after that. Each boy was determined that Dick's brother would hear a good debate the next week. Tommy could hardly wait to tell his father about the club's plans.

Tommy found it harder than ever to study that week. He wanted to spend every minute getting ready for the debate. There were many things that the other boys in the club could do better than he did. Although he was stronger than he used to be, he was still worn out before they began to feel tired. Often, too, he couldn't play in the more exciting games for fear he'd break his glasses.

"But a fellow doesn't need to be strong to be a good debater," he told himself. "And my glasses won't be in the way, either. This is my chance and I'm going to make the most of it."

154

He sat down at his desk and started to work. When had the pen been mightier than the sword? That would be the first question.

Histories had always been Tommy's favorite books. He had more than one of them on his shelf. He went through them now to find times when whole countries had been influenced by the words some great men had written. "The Declaration of Independence," he told himself. "I'll start off with that."

After he had thought up his own arguments, he thought up the arguments the other side would be likely to make. He planned how to answer them. The more he worked, the more interested he became.

WHAT SHOULD HE DO?

When the afternoon for the debate came, the boys were ready. All of them were eager to represent the Lightfoot Club when it started to have debates with other clubs.

"But Tommy will win first place," said Peter while they waited for the judge to arrive. "Even when he hasn't studied up in advance, he always out-argues us. And you know how he can make us do things his way. He'll make the judge think his way, too."

"He'll win first place when we debate the other clubs, too," said Bob.

Just then Dick Fulsom's brother arrived. "Good afternoon, gentlemen," he said, as if they were college men, all of them.

He took his place where Tommy usually stood. Then he took some slips from his pocket. "I am sure you will want to carry on this debate just as the literary societies in my college would do it. So I prepared these slips of paper which I'll put in my hat. Each of you will draw one. It will tell you which side you are to take."

Each of the boys came forward and drew out a slip. When Tommy's turn came he put his hand in the hat. He opened the slip and read it.

"But this says I must argue that the sword is mightier than the pen," he exclaimed. "I can't take that side. I don't believe it."

"That doesn't make any difference," the boys told him. "We don't care which side you really believe in. Just give us a good debate."

Tommy shook his head. "I couldn't argue for something I thought was wrong."

"You'll have to, now you've drawn that slip," said the judge. "It must be that or nothing."

"Then it will have to be nothing."

"You sound like a spoiled child. 'If I can't have the side I want, I won't play.'"

"Maybe I do, but I can't help it. I can't argue for something I don't believe in. It would be dishonest."

Some of the boys called him stubborn. Some

said he was a poor sport. He was going back on his friends. They made him feel very uncomfortable, but they couldn't change his mind. He didn't debate.

"What can we do with a fellow like Tommy?" asked Peter disgustedly. "Nothing. Just nothing. But the strange thing about it is—no matter how angry I get with him, I still like him."

General Lee Comes to Town

TOMMY WAS sure that nothing would ever make Professor Derry give his school a holiday, but he was mistaken. Wonderful news came over the telegraph wire one morning. The whole city rocked with excitement. General Robert E. Lee, the great leader of the Confederate army, was on his way to Savannah. He would stop over in Augusta to spend the night!

Professor Derry was as excited as any of the boys. "To see Robert E. Lee—that will be something for you to tell your grandchildren! Tomorrow morning there will be no school until after his train leaves."

Tommy could hardly sleep that night. At half past nine he heard the engine whistle. General Lee's train was coming. It would be at the station by now. The committee would be there to meet him. The general would be tired. He had had a long illness. No one else could see him tonight. But tomorrow——!

Long before train time the next morning the sidewalks were lined with people. Men were crowding to see their old commander. Women

and children wanted to greet their hero. The war was over. He was no longer a soldier. But he was still loved as no other man in the South had ever been loved.

Tommy could hardly wait for breakfast. As he left the house Joe joined him. They dashed down the street together. Suppose the general had left for the station earlier than had been expected! Suppose they had missed him!

They weren't too late. They had to wait and wait. The sun was hot. Mothers sat down on the curbs with their babies in their laps. Old soldiers leaned against the trees. Then word came from the hotel. General Lee was tired from his long trip. He wouldn't take the morning train. He was going to stay in Augusta all day.

The crowd cheered. Everyone started toward the hotel. Joe and Tommy found themselves being swept along by the crowd. Once Tommy almost lost his glasses. A woman beside him

161

bumped them when she tried to raise her arm. Tommy caught them just before they fell off.

"You'd better put them in your pocket," Joe said. "You don't need to see where you're going. You have to go where the crowd pushes you anyway. Ouch! Someone bumped me."

Tommy thought that his glasses were as safe on his face as they would be in his pocket. He grinned as he put them back on.

Finally the boys were in front of the hotel. The yard in front of it was packed with people, and the hotel itself seemed to be full, too.

A young man with pencil and paper in his hand pushed his way out of the hotel doorway. He smiled at Tommy, who was crowded up against the building.

"Did you see him? Did he talk with you?" everyone asked the young man.

The man took out his handkerchief and mopped his forehead. "Yes, I saw him," he answered. "There's the biggest crowd in there that this hotel ever has had. But the general takes time to speak with each person. He looks old and sick, but he's still a great man."

A woman next to Tommy looked down at her little boy. With one hand he clung to his mother's skirts. In the other hand he clutched a big bunch of roses.

"Don't forget," the woman was saying to her son, "when we get into the general's room, tell him that your name is Robert E. Lee Simpson. Then give him the flowers. You can always remember that you saw the great general you were named for."

The crowd at the door moved forward a few steps. Tommy lost sight of the woman and boy, as they edged forward.

Just then two old soldiers came through the doorway. One of them was wiping his eyes. Tommy heard him say, "Imagine General Lee remembering that I was wounded at Gettysburg! What a memory he has!"

Tommy turned to look at Joe. Joe wasn't smiling now. The boys were only a few steps from the door, but Joe shook his head.

"We'll never get in, Tommy," he said. "You and I are the wrong age. We're too young to have been soldiers, but we're too old to have been named for him. We won't get in."

"We can try," said Tommy. The crowd inched forward. Tommy turned to say something to Joe, but several strangers were in the way. Tommy knew that there was no use trying to stay with Joe.

He wormed his way through the crowd. Finally he was in the hall. Then he slipped into the room. At last two soldiers who had been talking to the general turned away. Tommy slipped into their place. The next moment he was standing by General Lee.

The general saw him and smiled. Then a group of men pushed forward. They pushed Tommy to one side. He had seen the general, so he was ready to go home. He didn't even try to find Joe, but started home alone.

The first book Tommy ever read himself had been about General George Washington. Then and there Washington had become his first hero. Now he had a second one. He had seen Robert E. Lee—not from far away, but close up. He had seen the kindness in Lee's face and also the sadness.

A lump came into Tommy's throat. It was hard to put into words exactly what he felt, but Father had trained him to try. Why were Washington and Lee great men? He puzzled it out as he walked home under the hot sun. They were both brave soldiers, but that wasn't all. No, indeed!

"It sounds preachy," he said to himself, "but

it is true, all the same. Both of them were ready to give themselves in war and in peace to the building up of their country. That's it."

He gave a satisfied sigh because he had figured it out. Then he hurried up the porch steps. "I wonder what Mother is going to have for dinner today."

Good-by to the Lightfoot Club

"I'M GOING to have a busy time this fall," Tommy told his mother. "You should see the long lessons in Greek and Latin Professor Derry is giving us! Besides that, the Lightfoot Club still has two more games to play. And there are those new books Father bought last week. I'll have to squeeze them in somewhere."

The first of the two games came the next afternoon. The Lightfoot boys lost it in the ninth inning. Peter, at second, muffed the ball when the bases were full.

"But we still have one more game," Tommy told his team.

He was busy with his plans as he walked home. "Maybe, if we shifted Peter from——"

Annie was waiting for him in the hall. "Tommy!" she said. "The most exciting thing has happened! Father has been asked to teach in the theological school at Columbia. How would you like to live in South Carolina?"

Tommy's thoughts came back from the baseball field with a jolt. Leave Augusta! Leave Professor Derry! Leave the Lightfoot Club!

"Are we really going?" he asked.

"I don't know. Father hasn't decided yet."

Tommy listened anxiously that night when Father prayed for guidance. The next afternoon and the next and the next, he asked Mother as soon as he came in from school, "Have you and Father decided yet?"

"Yes," she told him at last. "Father has told the school at Columbia that he will come. We shall have to move in a few weeks."

A few weeks! Tommy gave a sigh of relief. He could still play in the last game of the season for the Lightfoot team.

THE LAST GAME

The sun shone clear the next Saturday morning. "We won't have any rain to stop us today," Tommy told the girls happily.

"We're coming to watch you," Annie said.

The Blues came from the other side of town. They were a strong team. Tommy watched them anxiously as they came on the field. Their captain's fingers looked battered and out of shape.

"A good many ball players have fingers like that," Tommy thought. "It would be a good thing if we could all wear gloves. It would save a lot of sprained fingers."

Sometimes Tommy played center field, but today he was at shortstop. "Come on, boys," he

170

called as they ran out into the field. "Let's make this game a walkover."

But it wasn't a walkover at all. Both sides were retired with a blank for the first two innings. Then the Blues got a man on first base. The next player sent a daisy cutter to right field. It was a fine two-base hit. The first player came home. The next two men were out. The score was 1–0 in favor of the Blues.

When the Lightfoot boys went to bat, their luck changed, too. Joe made a fine hit over the center fielder's head and got to second base. Tommy hit an infield single which brought Joe to third. Henry came to bat. He struck at the ball twice but missed it. Then he sent a hot liner to third base. The third baseman muffed it, and the ball went far out into left field. Both Joe and Tommy came home. Tommy's team was ahead 2–1.

In the next inning the Blues made two runs.

The Lightfoot boys made another. The score was tied. After that, first one team, then the other would get ahead, but never by more than one run. When the last half of the eighth inning was over, the score was 7–6 in favor of the Lightfoot team.

"Let's keep it there!" called Tommy as they went out into the field for the last time.

The Blues' first man at bat went out. The next one reached first base. With a single the third player advanced him to second. Now their best hitter came to bat.

He didn't even try to swing at the first two balls. When the third came, he hit hard. The ball whizzed toward the shortstop. It was over his head. Tommy jumped as he reached for it. It was a fine catch, but the ball stung his hand so that he almost muffed it. He threw the ball to second. The Blue player was caught off base. A double play! The game was over!

The umpire called the final score. "Seven to six in favor of the Lightfoot team." How the club members cheered! They gave a special cheer, too, for Captain Wilson.

Tommy felt happy, but he was sad, too. He started home with his bat over his shoulder. His games with the Lightfoot Club were over.

Moving to Columbia

"I DON'T LIKE moving a bit," Tommy told his sisters. "It's as bad as spring housecleaning and getting ready for company rolled together."

"You haven't let it bother you too much," Annie answered. "All you did was to pack your books and your bat. Then you said, 'I'm ready.'"

"Well, I am."

Marion looked up from the trunk she was packing. She had been helping Mother ever since daybreak. "What about your clothes?" she asked.

Tommy looked sheepish. "I reckon I'll let you take care of them."

Marion laughed. "All right. You take care of Joseph. That will get both of you out from underfoot."

Tommy decided he would take Joseph for a ride on the streetcar. It would give him a chance to tell the driver good-by, too.

"I'm sorry you're leaving," the driver told him.

"I'm sorry, too," said Tommy.

But when they got back to the house nearly all the furniture was gone. The empty rooms looked so strange and unfriendly that he was glad when the time came to leave.

FIRST VIEW OF COLUMBIA

Aunt Marion and Jessie came down to the station to see them off. Father had gone on ahead. He met them at the station in Columbia. Soon they were driving to their new home. Tommy was busy trying to see both sides of the street.

176

For block after block there were no houses
at all—only charred ruins with heaps of black-
ened bricks and half-burned walls. Green vines,
weeds and even a few flowers were growing out
of the cluttered cellars.

"What happened?" asked Tommy. "It looks as if the whole city was burned."

"Most of it was," said Father. "It happened right at the end of the war. Some people say the Yankees burned it. Some say our own men started it to keep the enemy back. But fire and war always go together. Columbia was destroyed."

"Oh!" Tommy thought back to the war days when he was a small boy in Augusta. "And I thought we were in the middle of the war there," he remembered. He looked again at the ruins they were passing. "The people of Columbia know what war really is."

Father nodded. "It is suffering," he said, "and starvation and cruelty."

"Pray God," said Mother, "that it may never happen again."

Tommy was nearly fifteen now. He was beginning to think for himself. "That prayer isn't

178

quite right," he thought. He remembered the old proverb, "Heaven helps those who help themselves."

"I reckon that is it," he decided. They passed what had been a beautiful lawn. Now it was a mass of weeds choked with rubbish.

"Pray God," he murmured to himself, "that I may help keep war from ever happening again."

Princeton Days

TEEN-AGE Tommy had not yet won the struggle against poor health. He tried to start college at Davidson when he was seventeen, but the doctors sent him home. After another year he was stronger.

"You may try again," his father said. "There are many good schools. Maybe you would like to go to one of the northern colleges." So this time Tommy went to Princeton, in New Jersey.

There he soon became as busy as ever he had been when he was president of the Lightfoot Club. There were more debates and of course there was more baseball.

180

"I may not be strong enough yet to play on the team," he told himself, "but at least I can help clear the land for a diamond."

He learned a good deal, too, about a new game called football. He liked to plan plays for the team. Sometimes he would even referee a football game.

He started a new literary club. This meant a new constitution for him to write. He helped start a college newspaper, too.

Although Tommy was busy with extra activities, his schoolwork improved steadily. His health also was better than it ever had been.

As Tommy studied, he became more and more interested in history and government. He read everything he could on these subjects.

In his last year at Princeton, he was made editor of the college newspaper. It was his job to choose articles to print in this paper. Other students wrote about things that interested them. Then Tommy chose the best ones to print. Sometimes he printed one of his own articles on government.

It took a great deal of time and work to be a good editor. Tommy never forgot something that his father had taught him. "Be sure to say *exactly* what you mean," his father had told him. So when Tommy wrote for the college newspaper, he was careful to choose exactly the right words. He was proud of the paper.

As he worked and played, there was always a question in his mind. "After I leave college, what shall I do with my life?"

Then suddenly he found the answer. He had gone to the library to look up a quotation. A new magazine had just come in. He picked it up and began to read. It had come from England. It described the men who had been the heads of the English government. It told how they had made England what she was.

As Tommy read, his thoughts became clear. They weren't new thoughts exactly. For months they had been in the back of his mind.

Ever since he had written the constitution of the Lightfoot Club, he had liked to study the ways in which people could govern themselves. "What this magazine says is true," he told himself. "For good government there must be good leaders. And the United States needs them just as much as England does.

"I've been wondering what I'll do after I leave college. I'd like to become a good leader in the government."

The more he thought about it, the surer he became. "Of course it won't be easy. First I'll have to study. I must learn all the ways of good government. I must learn how to show these ways to other people. Maybe I'll write books or teach—or both. Maybe I'll become a senator or even a governor."

Half joking, half serious, he wrote the words down to see how they would look. Senator Tommy Wilson. Governor Tommy Wilson. "No, that isn't right. Tommy doesn't fit."

But he had another name—Woodrow. He tried again. Senator Woodrow Wilson. Governor Woodrow Wilson. That was better. He looked at the words with a grin.

Then Tommy became serious again. He turned back to the beginning of the article in the magazine. He read a few paragraphs. Then he thought about them. He read a few more paragraphs and thought about them.

When Tommy looked out the library window, he was surprised to see that it was getting dark. He had spent the whole afternoon reading and thinking about one article.

He hurried down the stairs and across the campus. Stars were coming out. A good fresh wind was blowing. Tommy felt as uplifted and free as the wind. His big question had been answered. He knew what he was going to do with his life.

Woodrow,
the Man

So Tommy Wilson, the boy, grew into Woodrow Wilson, the man. He studied good government. He wrote books about it. He taught it. He became President of Princeton University, then Governor of New Jersey. Finally, in 1913, he became President of the United States.

World War I broke out. President Wilson knew what war meant. He remembered the anxious days in Augusta. He remembered the black ruins of Columbia. He tried with all his heart and soul to keep it away from his country. At last he found that this was impossible.

"We must fight," he told his countrymen sorrowfully. "But if we go into this war heart and soul we shall win. And we can make it a war that will end all wars."

He began, even before the war was over, to plan a way to end wars. He explained his plan to Congress. He explained it to the people of the United States and to the whole world.

"There was a time," he said, "when every man fought his neighbor. Now neighbors have learned to live together in peace. Here in America our states have learned to live together in one country. Now the countries, too, must unite. We must have a League of Nations."

The war ended. The victorious allies made plans for a meeting where they would draw up a treaty of peace. Who should be sent to represent the United States?

"I shall go myself," said Woodrow Wilson.

No President had ever left the United States before while he was in office. Many people didn't like the idea. "A President's place is in his own country," they said.

"I *must* go," President Wilson insisted. "I must show the world how a League of Nations can keep the world at peace."

THE LEAGUE OF NATIONS

The people of Europe were tired of war, too. They gathered in crowds to cheer Wilson on. They loved him as, years before, the people of Augusta had loved General Lee.

Wherever he went—France, England, Italy— the same thing happened. Mothers brought their children to see the great man. Even the poorest home had his picture on the wall. Everywhere crowds cheered him. "He will make the world free!" the people cried.

But when the Peace Conference began, his popularity died. The world was not ready for the League as he planned it. To make it a success the nations of the world would have to be unselfish.

The politicians at the Peace Conference couldn't understand this. It seemed more sensible and patriotic for each one to grab as much land and money as he could for his own people.

President Wilson knew this was a sure way to bring on more wars. He knew, too, that many parts of the peace treaty were unwise. "After the League of Nations is started, though," he told himself, "it will straighten these things out."

He was still hopeful for the future when he returned to America. But there he found a new disappointment. Not even his own people were ready for the League.

"Why," they asked, "should the United States get mixed up again in the quarrels of Europe? Let Europe take care of herself. We'll take care of ourselves."

"But that is the way wars begin," Wilson insisted. "The United States cannot keep apart from the rest of the world—not in these days. There must be a place where all the nations can come and work out their problems together. We must have a League of Nations."

The people of the United States didn't agree with him.

"It is because they don't understand," he decided. "I must explain it all again. I'll make a trip across the country and hold meetings in every state."

He was an old man now and very tired. His doctor shook his head when he heard what the President wanted to do.

"You shouldn't try it," said the doctor.

"I must," said President Wilson.

He started on his long, hard trip. At first it looked as if his plan might work. As a boy, Tommy had usually been able to make people see

things his way. As President Wilson, he still had the same skill. But halfway through the trip his health gave way. Ill and helpless, he was carried back to Washington. His fight to have the United States join the League of Nations was lost. A few years later, in 1924, he died.

For a while it seemed that all for which he had worked died, too. The League of Nations, without America, was weak and powerless. At last his worst fears were realized. The world was caught up in another war.

But when World War II was over, Wilson's dream once more came into being. This time the organization was called the United Nations instead of the League of Nations, but its object was much the same. It was created to lead the world once more along the paths that Woodrow Wilson planned—toward freedom for all and a just and lasting peace.

More About This Book

WHEN WOODROW WILSON LIVED

1856   THOMAS WOODROW WILSON WAS BORN IN STAUNTON, VIRGINIA, DECEMBER 28.

There were thirty-one states in the Union.

Franklin D. Pierce was President.

The population of the country was about 28,140,000.

1856–   AFTER TWO YEARS IN STAUNTON, TOMMY LIVED
1870   IN AUGUSTA, GEORGIA.

Eleven states seceded from the Union and formed the Confederate States of America, 1860-1861.

The first transcontinental telegraph was completed, 1861.

The War between the States was fought, 1861-1865.

The Emancipation Proclamation was issued, 1863.

The first transcontinental railroad was completed, 1869.

| 1870– | TOMMY COMPLETED HIGH SCHOOL AND GRADU- |
| 1879 | ATED FROM PRINCETON UNIVERSITY. |

Alexander G. Bell invented the telephone, 1876.

Rutherford B. Hayes became President, 1877.

Thomas Edison invented the phonograph, 1878, and the electric light bulb, 1879.

| 1879– | WILSON WAS A STUDENT, LAWYER, TEACHER, |
| 1913 | WRITER, AND GOVERNOR. |

Clara Barton founded the American Red Cross, 1881.

The Spanish-American War was fought, 1898.

Wilbur and Orville Wright flew the first heavier-than-air aircraft, 1903.

Robert Peary discovered the North Pole, 1909.

| 1913– | WILSON SERVED TWO TERMS AS PRESIDENT |
| 1924 | AND AFTERWARDS RETIRED. |

The Panama Canal was completed and opened to world traffic, 1914.

The United States entered World War I, 1917.

World War I ended, 1918.

The League of Nations was formed, 1920.

194

1924 WILSON DIED FEBRUARY 3, IN WASHINGTON, D.C., AFTER THREE YEARS RETIREMENT.

There were forty-eight states in the Union.

Calvin Coolidge was President.

The population of the country was about 112,500,000.

DO YOU REMEMBER?

1. Why was Thomas Woodrow Wilson called Tommy when he was a boy?

2. What important news did Tommy overhear when he climbed one of the gateposts at his home?

3. Who was Tommy's father and how did he serve as a community leader?

4. How did Tommy and Joe Lamar happen to see men leaving to join the Confederate Army?

5. How did Tommy manage to get to take a horseback ride even though horses were scarce?

6. What important events finally brought the War between the States to an end?

7. How did Tommy and his friends form the Lightfoot Club, and who became president?

195

8. What happened when the boys stayed away from school to watch a circus parade?

9. Why did Tommy refuse to debate that the sword is mightier than the pen?

10. How did Tommy get to see Robert E. Lee when Lee came to Augusta?

11. What prayer did Tommy utter when the family first moved to Columbia?

12. What activities did Tommy carry on while he attended Princeton University?

13. What important positions did Woodrow Wilson hold during his lifetime?

14. What important organization did Wilson help to found after World War I?

IT'S FUN TO LOOK UP THESE THINGS

1. Where is Staunton, Virginia, the city where Wilson was born?

2. What other schools besides Princeton University did Wilson attend?

3. Where did Wilson practice law for a short period of time?

4. What was the famous Quad Plan which Wilson started at Princeton University?

5. When did fighting cease in World War I, and how is the date celebrated today?

6. What important Nobel Prize was awarded to Wilson following World War I?

7. What other countries besides the United States helped to found the League of Nations?

INTERESTING THINGS YOU CAN DO

1. Make a list of Presidents besides Wilson who were born in Virginia.

2. Prepare a report on the principal causes of World War I.

3. Find out what event caused the United States to enter World War I.

4. Make a list of popular songs which were sung during World War I.

5. Explain why the League of Nations lasted only a short period of time.

6. Collect pictures of Wilson as President for a display on the bulletin board.

197

OTHER BOOKS YOU MAY ENJOY READING

America Travels, Alice Dalgliesh. Macmillan.

George Washington: Boy Leader, Augusta Stevenson. Trade and School Editions, Bobbs-Merrill.

Heroes, Heroines and Holidays, Eleanor Thomas. Ginn.

Lee, the Gallant General, Jeanette Eaton. Morrow.

Pets at the White House, Carl Carmer. Dutton.

Rainbow Round the World, Elizabeth Yates. Bobbs-Merrill.

Story of the Presidents, Maud and Miska Petersham. Macmillan.

They Lived in the White House, Frances Cavanah. Macrae Smith.

INTERESTING WORDS IN THIS BOOK

adjourn (ă jûrn′) : end a meeting

aisle (īl) : passageway, usually between rows of seats, as in a church or school

bale: large package of compressed raw material, bound tightly and often wrapped

banister (băn′ĭs tẽr) : railing at the side of an open stairway

198

beeline: direct or straight line

boll (bōl) : seed pod of cotton plant, which bursts open when cotton is ripe

brier (brī'ẽr) : bush with woody stems and branches covered with thorns

campus: grounds of a college or school

catechism (kăt'ĕ kĭz'm) : book or manual filled with questions and answers, used for providing religious instruction within a church

charred: burned black but not turned to ashes

congregation (kŏng'grĕ gā'shŭn) : group of people who belong to or attend a certain church

constitution (kŏn'stĭ tū'shŭn) : statement of purposes and rules or laws of an organization, a state, or a nation

debate: engages in an argument for or against a certain subject according to a set of rules

discipline (dis'ĭ plĭn) : enforcement of good behavior, often by rules

elder: person in certain churches who shares with other persons, including the minister, in deciding how the church should be run

fidgety: restless, impatient, nervous

gable: three-cornered top end of a building, with sides formed by sloping portions of a roof

gallery: upper floor of a building located over the back part of first floor, balcony

199

grid: grating or coarse screen used to sort out or hold back larger particles, while allowing smaller particles to fall through

moderator (mŏd′ēr ā′tēr) : person in charge of a meeting, chairman

parliamentary law (pär lĭ mĕn′tȧ rĭ) : rules of order, rules for carrying on a meeting

pine tags: needles from pine trees that have fallen to the ground and formed a thick covering

quotation (kwȯ tā′shŭn) : actual words or statement taken from the writings or sayings of another

snicker: short, smothered laugh

sprig: twig or small branch of a plant

steamcars: railroad cars

stubble: stumps of grainstalks, a few inches high, left in a field after the grain has been cut

surrender (sŭ rĕn′dēr) : yield, give up

theological (thē′ȯ lŏj′ĭ kăl) : referring to religion, often applied to a special college or university where ministers are trained

truant (trōō′ănt) : child who stays away from school without permission

unwary: not suspecting, unguarded

vestibule (vĕs′tĭ būl) : entrance hall, room between outer door and inner part of a building

200